I am the Vine, you are the branches
Fz. 15:15

Presented To:

Nancy Sterling

From:

Date:

Sept. 17, 2015

DISCIPLE *of* CHRIST

EDUCATION IN VIRTUE ™

LIFE OF CHRIST

LECTIO DIVINA
JOURNAL

Sister John Dominic Rasmussen, O.P.

LUMEN
ECCLESIAE
PRESS

Published by Lumen Ecclesiae Press
    4101 East Joy Road
    Ann Arbor, Michigan 48105

Cover Design: Anthem Branding, Boulder, CO
Cover Layout: Amy Beers
Artist: Sr. Emmanuel Gross, O.P.
Book Design Layout: Linda Kelly
Copy Editor: Claudia Volkman
Copyrights and Permissions: Linda Kelly and Kristina Smith
Contributors: Sister Teresa Benedicta Block, O.P. and Bernadette Miller

Requests for permission to make copies of any part of the work should be directed to: info@educationinvirtue.com.

For more information: educationinvirtue.com

Nihl Obstat: Monsignor Robert Lunsford
                   Censor Librorium

Imprimatur: † Earl Boyea
                   Bishop of Lansing
                   June 22, 2015

Printed with Ecclesiastical Permission. Most Reverend Earl Boyea, Bishop of Lansing. June 22, 2015.

ISBN 978-0-9899921-5-2

First Printing
Printed in the United States of America

Foreword

Sister John Dominic Rasmussen, O.P., has provided Catholic educators and young people with an excellent tool in her text *Life of Christ, Lectio Divina Journal*. More than a textbook, it introduces young people to a prayerful reading and understanding the life of Jesus as recorded in the gospels. It provides them an opportunity to know Jesus in a personal way, to listen to His voice as they reflect and pray and to respond to His invitation to follow Him through resolutions and the practice of the virtues.

This journal enables the prayer of St. Richard of Chichester to be realized in the lives of those students who use it: "O most merciful Redeemer, friend and brother, may I know you more closely, love you more dearly, follow you more nearly."

I pray that this work will achieve wide circulation and lead many young people to a personal encounter with Jesus and the fullness of life He offers us.

Most Reverent Earl Boyea,
Bishop of Lansing

Christ and the Apostles, (I am the Life), Greek School, (17th century) /
Byzantine Museum, Athens, Greece / De Agostini Picture Library / G. Dagli
Orti / Bridgeman Images

— *"Who do you say that I am?"* (Mark 8:27) —

To live as a disciple of Christ, one must first know the Person of Jesus Christ and answer with conviction the same question Jesus asked His first disciples, "Who do you say that I am?" (Mark 8:27). This knowledge is learned by encountering the Word of God and remaining with Jesus (see John 15:4), as did Mary and His disciples.

Mary, the mother of Jesus, was the first to live with Jesus and to show us how to be fully open and receptive to God's will. At the Annunciation she said "Yes" and, by the overshadowing of the Holy Spirit, Jesus was conceived in her womb. Like all mothers, Mary wondered what her child would be like and kept everything in her heart — pondering the meaning (see Luke 2: 19, 51).

When Jesus began teaching and preaching, He taught the conditions of discipleship, which included the daily taking up of one's cross as well as not being ashamed of His words (see Luke 9:23–27). Furthermore, Jesus taught that a disciple is one who hears the word of God and acts on it (see Luke 8:21). This same message resonates in His teaching on the vine and the branches. To remain in Jesus is to be grafted onto the vine so that His words remain in us and, in Him, we bear much fruit (see John 15:1–15).

By listening and remaining in Jesus, a disciple is able to experience His friendship and know all that His Father revealed. "I have called you friends because I have told you everything I have heard from my Father" (John 15:15). Living in friendship with Jesus can be difficult; as He told His disciples, "If the world hates you, realize that it hated me first" (John 15:18). A disciple does not find his happiness in the world, but only by remaining in Him who first loved us (see 1 John 4:10).

Mary was the first in time to witness the joy of acting upon God's word (Luke 1:46–47) and trusting in her Son (John 2:5). Therefore, her presence in the Upper Room with the disciples was one of hope, filled with anticipation for the coming of the Holy Spirit (see Acts 1:13–14) who would descend upon them and fill their hearts with the fire of His love (see Acts 2:1–4). Filled with the Spirit, they were empowered to announce the Good News and to courageously be His witnesses.

Just as Mary and the disciples encountered Jesus by remaining in Him and listening to and acting upon His words, you, too, are called to this same friendship and personal relationship with the Person of Jesus Christ. May your heart burn within as He speaks to you and opens the Scriptures for you (see Luke 24:32), and may you be able to answer His question to you "Who do you say that I am?" (Mark 8:27).

— How to Use This Journal —

As you use this journal and open your mind and heart to the Holy Spirit, you will begin to experience a closer relationship with the Person of Jesus Christ. This experience will be more than just journaling but will also be entering into a lifelong conversation with God. The more you ponder His Word — slowly meditating on the questions and listening to what Christ desires to communicate to you, the deeper your friendship with Jesus will become. Avoid the temptation to rush through the pages but instead relish the time you have with Christ.

 In a Spirit of Silence, place yourself in the presence of God and recite the prayer to the Holy Spirit.

 Read the Scripture Passages in sequence and use the questions to guide you in your prayerful conversation with the Lord.

 Living as a Disciple of Christ icon suggests ways you can deepen your commitment to live as a disciple of Christ.

 Silently Study the Religious Artwork and let the image help you visualize the scripture passage.

 My Meditation is a place for you to write your own meditation after pondering the Word of God and gazing upon the religious art.

 Gratitude Log enables you to express praise to God for a grace you've received.

 My Life in Christ is an opportunity for you to journal your personal commitment to act upon God's Word and live as a disciple of Christ.

JESUS, ANNOUNCED AND ADORED

JESUS ENTERS HIS PUBLIC MINISTRY

JESUS THE TEACHER

JESUS OUT ON MISSION

— Announcement of the Birth of John —

Father, anoint me with Your Holy Spirit so that as I read Your
Eternal Word, it may penetrate my whole being and transform me
into a faithful disciple of Christ.
Amen.

God's Word strikes the heart. What word or phrase touched your heart?

Love... God is love

Zechariah and his wife, Elizabeth, were "righteous in the eyes of God." Describe how they lived. How were they similar to Abraham and Sarah (see Genesis 17:15–21)?

- Followed the laws - commandments & ordinances
- Both couples were old & both laughed at the prospect

Write down Zechariah's response to the angel.

"How shall I know this?"

TODAY'S DATE 9-17-15

Zechariah was disturbed by the presence of the angel, Gabriel, and failed to believe the angel's word. Gabriel declared that Zechariah would remain speechless (mute) until the prophecy was fulfilled. How did this enable Zechariah to increase in faith and trust in God?

· Contemplation

Zechariah had trouble believing the message announced by the angel, possibly because it seemed too good to be true. Ask Jesus this question in prayer: "Jesus, what good things do You especially want me to believe about You?" Write down what you hear Him say.

I think Jesus wants me to believe that I can trust in Him completely

Write a prayer asking God to increase your faith and trust in Him.

Dear Jesus,
Please help me to trust in you & to have me follow your will instead of my will.

Annunciation to Saint Zacharias by the Archangel Gabriel of the Birth of His Son John the Baptist / Andrea Miglionico / Photo © Tarker / Bridgeman Images

Silently study the painting and recall the Scripture passage. Who is depicted? What other details do you notice?

Zacharias & the Archangel Gabriel

2. questioning m hand motion — "Who? Me?"

Describe Zechariah's pose and the expression on his face. Explain why he is pointing to himself.

At times it can be difficult to trust in God. How does this image reflect the fears and anxieties of daily life?

Being uncertain, questioning..

TODAY'S DATE 9-7-15

✝ My Meditation

I need to trust in the Trinity & my Guardian Angel more completely and to believe that the Blessed Mother petitions to Jesus for me.

🙌 With Gratitude I Praise You, God, for

creating the world, loving us enough to come down from Heaven to die for my sins, and giving us the Holy Spirit to guide me.

— Annunciation and Incarnation —

Father, anoint me with Your Holy Spirit so that as I read Your Eternal Word, it may penetrate my whole being and transform me into a faithful disciple of Christ.

Amen.

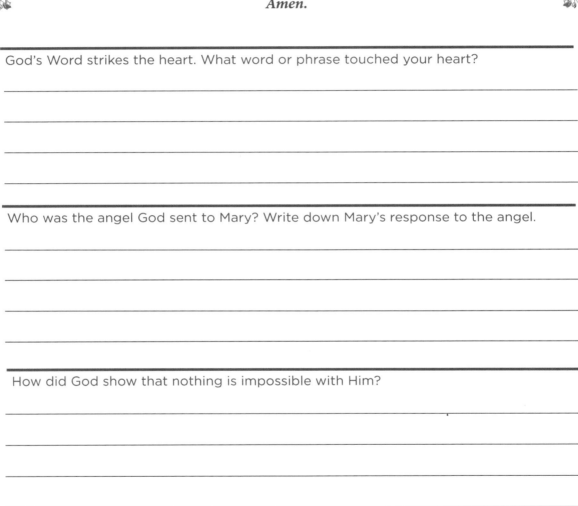

God's Word strikes the heart. What word or phrase touched your heart?

_____

_____

_____

_____

Who was the angel God sent to Mary? Write down Mary's response to the angel.

_____

_____

_____

_____

How did God show that nothing is impossible with Him?

_____

_____

_____

_____

To obey means "to hear." Describe how the virtues of docility and humility enabled Mary to obey God (see pages 323–326).

_____

_____

_____

_____

Are you ever afraid to say yes to God? Why? Ask Jesus this question: "Lord, what should I do when I am afraid of saying yes to You?" Write down what you hear Him say.

_____

_____

_____

_____

_____

 Memorize the following verse (Luke 1:38) and seek to imitate Mary's yes to God in your daily life.

Mary said, "Behold, I am the handmaid of the Lord.
May it be done to me according to your word."

The Annunciation, Tanner, Henry Ossawa / Philadelphia Museum of Art / Bridgeman Images

Silently study the painting. What scriptural moment is occurring and who is present? How do the details (such as color) enhance the painting's tone and feeling?

_____

_____

_____

Describe Mary's expression and pose. Contrast Mary's expression and pose to the figure of the angel.

_____

_____

_____

Yellow is a predominant color used in art to symbolize life, joy, happiness, and hope. How does the use of this color capture the Annunciation?

_____

_____

_____

✝ My Meditation

_____

_____

_____

_____

_____

_____

_____

_____

_____

_____

_____

_____

_____

_____

_____

_____

_____

_____

_____

_____

_____

_____

🙌 With Gratitude I Praise You, God, for

_____

_____

_____

— Visitation (Magnificat) —

Father, anoint me with Your Holy Spirit so that as I read Your Eternal Word, it may penetrate my whole being and transform me into a faithful disciple of Christ.

Amen.

God's Word strikes the heart. What word or phrase touched your heart?

_____

_____

_____

_____

The angel Gabriel told Mary that her cousin Elizabeth was pregnant. Why do you think Mary went in haste to see her cousin?

_____

_____

_____

_____

How did the babe in Elizabeth's womb respond at the sound of Mary's voice?

_____

_____

_____

_____

TODAY'S DATE _____

Describe the feelings experienced in this meeting. What virtues do you recognize (see pages 323-326)?

_____

_____

_____

_____

Ask this question in prayer: "Lord, how are You calling me to bring the Good News to others?" Write down what you hear the Lord saying to you.

_____

_____

_____

_____

_____

_____

Generosity is giving of oneself in a willing and cheerful manner for the good of others. List several ways you need to be more generous.

_____

_____

_____

_____

_____

Silently study the painting. What is the depicted Gospel narrative and who is the main subject?

_____

_____

_____

_____

Describe the painting's colors. What tone, feeling, or message does this coloring evoke?

_____

_____

_____

_____

What do the figures' hands and overall pose reveal about their relationship and their encounter?

_____

_____

_____

_____

_____

_____

_____

Mary and Elizabeth, Hawksley, Dorothy Webster / Private Collection / Photo © The Maas Gallery, London / Bridgeman Images

✝ My Meditation

_____

_____

_____

_____

_____

_____

_____

_____

_____

_____

_____

_____

_____

_____

_____

_____

_____

_____

With Gratitude I Praise You, God, for

_____

_____

_____

— Birth of John (Benedictus) —

Father, anoint me with Your Holy Spirit so that as I read Your Eternal Word, it may penetrate my whole being and transform me into a faithful disciple of Christ.

Amen.

God's Word strikes the heart. What word or phrase touched your heart?

_____

_____

_____

_____

Zechariah had spent months in silence. After he wrote the name of his son, he could speak. What was significant about his first words?

_____

_____

_____

_____

When we are silent, we are better able to listen and see things more clearly. Describe how silence prepared Zechariah to accept God's will.

_____

_____

_____

_____

How can silence help you to deepen your faith and trust and listen to God?

_____

_____

_____

_____

Ask this question in prayer: "Jesus, what do You want to say to me as I listen to You in the silence of my heart?" Write down what you hear Him say.

_____

_____

_____

_____

_____

_____

To listen to God, it is important to limit the voluntary distractions. Make an effort to unplug from one of your devices. Write down how you plan to limit the use.

_____

_____

_____

_____

The Naming of John the Baptist, Angelico, Fra (Guido di Pietro) / Museo di San Marco dell'Angelico, Florence, Italy / Bridgeman Images

Silently study the painting. What might Zechariah be writing? How do the women react to what he is doing? Look at their gestures and expressions.

_____

_____

_____

Zechariah is dressed in red. Why is this significant?

_____

_____

_____

Silence aids in listening. How is silence represented in this painting?

_____

_____

_____

✝ My Meditation

_____
_____
_____
_____
_____
_____
_____
_____
_____
_____
_____
_____
_____
_____
_____
_____
_____
_____
_____
_____

🙏 With Gratitude I Praise You, God, for

_____
_____
_____
_____

— Joseph Learns of the Incarnation —

Father, anoint me with Your Holy Spirit so that as I read Your Eternal Word, it may penetrate my whole being and transform me into a faithful disciple of Christ.

Amen.

God's Word strikes the heart. What word or phrase touched your heart?

_____

_____

_____

_____

Joseph had decided to divorce Mary quietly. What does this reveal about Joseph's character?

_____

_____

_____

_____

An angel appeared to Joseph in a dream. What was his response to the message? How was Joseph's response different from Zechariah'?

_____

_____

_____

_____

MATTHEW 1:18-25

St. Matthew references the words of the prophet Isaiah (Isaiah 7:14). How was this fulfilled?

_____

_____

_____

_____

"Emmanuel" means *God is with us*. "Jesus, what do You want me to learn by Joseph's trust in the angel's message and Your name meaning 'God is with us?'" Write down what He says to you.

_____

_____

_____

_____

_____

_____

Spend time reflecting upon the ways that "God is with us." How does this truth increase your faith and hope in God's loving plan for your life?

_____

_____

_____

_____

_____

Silently study the painting. What is the Gospel narrative? Who is present? How does the artist depict the dream?

_____

_____

_____

_____

Describe the actions of the angels, especially the angel speaking to Joseph. Angels are messengers of God. How is this shown?

_____

_____

_____

The Most Holy Trinity is visible in the painting. Describe the actions and physical characteristics of God the Father and God the Holy Spirit. Where is God the Son?

_____

_____

_____

The Dream of St. Joseph, Giordano, Luca / Indianapolis Museum of Art, USA / Martha Delzell Memorial Fund / Bridgeman Images

✝ My Meditation

_____

_____

_____

_____

_____

_____

_____

_____

_____

_____

_____

_____

_____

_____

_____

_____

_____

_____

_____

🙌 With Gratitude I Praise You, God, for

_____

_____

_____

— Birth of Christ —

Father, anoint me with Your Holy Spirit so that as I read Your
Eternal Word, it may penetrate my whole being and transform me
into a faithful disciple of Christ.

Amen.

God's Word strikes the heart. What word or phrase touched your heart?

_____

_____

_____

_____

In response to the decree of Caesar Augustus, Joseph and Mary traveled to Bethlehem to be enrolled in the census. What does this show about respecting those in authority?

_____

_____

_____

_____

Describe how the journey was difficult for Joseph and Mary.

_____

_____

_____

_____

LUKE 2:1-7

Read Luke 9:57–58. From the moment of His birth, Jesus had "nowhere to lay His head." His kingdom was not of this world. As His disciples, how do we imitate His focus on heaven and what virtue sustains us (see pages 323-326)?

_____

_____

_____

_____

Ask this question in prayer: "Jesus, You were born in a stable because there was no room in the inn. How can I open my heart to welcome You today?" Write down what He says to you.

_____

_____

_____

_____

_____

Jesus experienced rejection even before His birth. This pattern continues today. Man has free will, and he can freely choose to close the door of his heart to Jesus. Spend a few moments praying for one person to say "yes" to His love and to open their heart to Him. Write down your prayer.

_____

_____

_____

_____

Nativity, Loo, Carle van (1705-65) / Musee de Picardie, Amiens, France / Bridgeman Images

Silently study the painting. Who are the central figures? How are we made aware of their importance?

_____

_____

_____

_____

How does this painting capture the peace and serenity of Mary? Does it stir inner peace within your heart?

_____

_____

_____

_____

✝ My Meditation

_____

_____

_____

_____

_____

_____

_____

_____

_____

_____

_____

_____

_____

_____

_____

_____

_____

_____

🙌 With Gratitude I Praise You, God, for

_____

_____

_____

— Jesus' Birth Is Revealed to the Shepherds —

*Father, anoint me with Your Holy Spirit so that as I read Your
Eternal Word, it may penetrate my whole being and transform me
into a faithful disciple of Christ.*

Amen.

God's Word strikes the heart. What word or phrase touched your heart?

_____

_____

_____

The angel of the Lord appeared to the shepherds. What pattern do you see in each greeting — Zechariah, Mary, Joseph, and shepherds?

_____

_____

_____

How were the virtues of docility, obedience, and faith shown in Mary, Joseph, and the shepherd's responses?

_____

_____

_____

How did the shepherds respond to the message? How was their response the same as Mary's response?

_____

_____

_____

Imagine you were with the shepherds. How would you have reacted?

_____

_____

_____

_____

"Lord, Your mother pondered — reflected upon — all these events in her heart. What do I need to silently reflect upon in my life so I may respond in obedience to Your will? Show me how I can be more docile, humble, and faithful." Write down what He says to you.

_____

_____

_____

_____

_____

The shepherds responded to the invitation of the angels to go and see the child. As a disciple of Christ, you are called to announce the presence of Jesus to others. Write about a time you told someone about Jesus.

_____

_____

_____

_____

The Adoration of the Shepherds, Reni, Guido / Pushkin Museum, Moscow, Russia / Bridgeman Images

Silently study this painting. Who is present and what are they doing? (Be sure to look through the window.)

_____

_____

In what two figures is the color white dominant? What might be the significance of their shared coloring? Think about the symbolism of the lamb.

_____

_____

_____

Witnessing the prayerfulness of each person stirs devotion and piety. What thoughts and emotions do you experience? How does it help you pray?

_____

_____

_____

✝ My Meditation

_____
_____
_____
_____
_____
_____
_____
_____
_____
_____
_____
_____
_____
_____
_____
_____
_____
_____
_____

🙌 With Gratitude I Praise You, God, for

_____
_____
_____

— Presentation —

*Father, anoint me with Your Holy Spirit so that as I read Your
Eternal Word, it may penetrate my whole being and transform me
into a faithful disciple of Christ.*

Amen.

God's Word strikes the heart. What word or phrase touched your heart?

_____

_____

_____

_____

Joseph and Mary had journeyed to Bethlehem in obedience to the civil law. Then they
presented Jesus in the Temple according to the law of Moses. Describe how they
fulfilled the law.

_____

_____

_____

_____

How did Simeon respond when he saw Jesus? How did he describe Him?

_____

_____

_____

_____

Why do you think Simeon said Jesus would be a sign that will be contradicted?

_____
_____
_____
_____

"Jesus, Anna spent time in the temple worshiping You and after encountering You, she spoke about You to everyone. How are You leading me closer to You so I may be a witness and proclaim Your name?" Write down what He says to you.

_____
_____
_____
_____
_____

Joseph and Mary presented Jesus in the temple to fulfill the law and to dedicate their Son to God. This was an act of love and obedience. Describe a time when you performed an act of love and were obedient.

_____
_____
_____
_____

The Presentation in the Temple, from a series of prints made by the Arundel Society (chromolitho), Angelico, Fra / Bridgeman Imagesw

Silently study the painting. What Gospel narrative is shown and what figures are present? (Saint Peter of Verona is the Dominican priest martyred by an axe to his skull.]

_____

_____

_____

Read Luke 2:33–38. Mary's hands are central to this painting. How do they express the emotions in her heart?

_____

_____

Simeon and Anna had been waiting patiently to see the Messiah. Study their expressions and gestures. How do they reveal their emotions and reactions to the depicted narrative?

_____

_____

_____

TODAY'S DATE _____

✝ My Meditation

_____

_____

_____

_____

_____

_____

_____

_____

_____

_____

_____

_____

_____

_____

_____

_____

_____

_____

🙌 With Gratitude I Praise You, God, for

_____

_____

_____

— Visit of the Magi —

*Father, anoint me with Your Holy Spirit so that as I read Your
Eternal Word, it may penetrate my whole being and transform me
into a faithful disciple of Christ.*

Amen.

God's Word strikes the heart. What word or phrase touched your heart?

_____

_____

_____

_____

The shepherds and Israelites learned of Christ's birth through an angel. How did God draw the Magi to His Son?

_____

_____

_____

_____

Herod was troubled by the question of the Magi searching to give homage to the King of the Jews. Describe his action and the sins he committed.

_____

_____

_____

_____

When the Magi saw Jesus and Mary, they prostrate themselves. Why do you think they reacted this way? What happened in their hearts?

_____

_____

_____

_____

Ask this question in prayer: "Lord, what can I do to be more open so that I, like Joseph, can hear You speaking to me — that I may do what You ask of me?" Write down what He says to you.

_____

_____

_____

_____

_____

Upon seeing the child Jesus with His mother, the Magi kneel in reverence and awe. They offer gifts of gold, frankincense, and myrrh. The gifts Jesus wants us to bring Him are our sins and weaknesses. This is why He became man and died for our sins. Think of one sin you struggle most with and surrender it to Jesus.

The Adoration of the Magi, Granger, Jean Pierre / Musee de la Ville de Paris, Musee du Petit-Palais, France / Bridgeman Images

Silently study the painting. Who is present and what are they doing?

_____

_____

_____

How does the artist draw your attention to the Christ Child? How is He distinguished from those surrounding Him?

_____

_____

_____

The Magi had followed the light of the star of Bethlehem to the Christ Child. What is the meaning/purpose of the Christ Child's gesture toward them? What does it reveal about His nature?

_____

_____

_____

_____

✝ My Meditation

_____
_____
_____
_____
_____
_____
_____
_____
_____
_____
_____
_____
_____
_____
_____
_____
_____
_____
_____
_____

🙌 With Gratitude I Praise You, God, for

_____
_____
_____

MATTHEW 2:13–18

— Flight into Egypt and Massacre of the Holy Innocents —

Father, anoint me with Your Holy Spirit so that as I read Your Eternal Word, it may penetrate my whole being and transform me into a faithful disciple of Christ.

Amen.

God's Word strikes the heart. What word or phrase touched your heart?

_____

_____

_____

_____

An angel of the Lord appeared again to Joseph in a dream. Describe his response. What virtue do you see in Joseph (see pages 323-326)?

_____

_____

_____

_____

Describe Herod's actions and the sins/vices he manifested.

_____

_____

_____

_____

How did other people suffer because of Herod's sins?

_____

_____

_____

_____

Ask this question in prayer: "Jesus, Messiah, King of Kings, Lord of Lords, is there a part of my heart filled with pride like Herod? How can I be more humble to offer homage upon seeing You?" Write down what you hear Him say to you.

_____

_____

_____

_____

_____

Herod was furious when he was deceived by the Magi. The fact that he had innocent baby boys killed shows the depth of his anger and pride. It is important to release anger from your heart. Spend time in quiet prayer and release any grudges, hurt feelings, or anger from your heart.

The Flight into Egypt, Francken, Frans & Govaerts, Abraham / Johnny van Haeften Gallery, London, UK / Bridgeman Images

Silently study the painting. Who is present and what are they doing? The painting is dense with detail, so how does the artist draw your attention to the main elements?

_____

_____

_____

Why are there babies lying on the side of the road? What might be the connection between them and Mary and Jesus' red clothing? Describe how Joseph is holding Jesus.

_____

_____

_____

After contemplating the painting's details and elements, what thoughts and emotions stir within your heart?

_____

_____

✝ My Meditation

_____

_____

_____

_____

_____

_____

_____

_____

_____

_____

_____

_____

_____

_____

_____

_____

_____

_____

_____

_____

_____

🙌 With Gratitude I Praise You, God, for

_____

_____

_____

— Return to Nazareth —

*Father, anoint me with Your Holy Spirit so that as I read Your
Eternal Word, it may penetrate my whole being and transform me
into a faithful disciple of Christ.*

Amen.

God's Word strikes the heart. What word or phrase touched your heart?

_____

_____

_____

_____

How did Joseph know it was safe to return to Nazareth?

_____

_____

_____

_____

Describe the pattern of holiness you see in Joseph as he took care of Mary and Jesus.

_____

_____

_____

_____

Joseph trusted in God and believed the message of the angel. How would you have reacted if you were Joseph?

_____

_____

_____

_____

Are you afraid to trust God at times? Ask Jesus this question in prayer: "Lord, how can I increase my trust in You?" Write down what He says.

_____

_____

_____

_____

_____

The theological virtue of faith enables one to know God and all He has revealed. Joseph's faith was constantly tested and yet he always listened and believed in the message of his dreams or the angels. Write a prayer asking God to increase your faith.

_____

_____

_____

_____

Silently study the painting. Who is present? How does the artist show that they are on a journey?

_____

_____

What is the tone and overall expression of the painting? Study the colors, composition, and movement of the painting.

_____

_____

_____

St. Joseph is picking fruit from the tree for his family. What does this teach us about God's creation and our relationship with it?

_____

_____

_____

The Rest on the Return From Egypt, Barocci or Baroccio, Federico Fiori / Private Collection / Photo © Christie's Images / Bridgeman Images

✝ My Meditation

_____
_____
_____
_____
_____
_____
_____
_____
_____
_____
_____
_____
_____
_____
_____
_____
_____
_____
_____

🙌 With Gratitude I Praise You, God, for

_____
_____
_____
_____

— The Child Jesus —

Father, anoint me with Your Holy Spirit so that as I read Your Eternal Word, it may penetrate my whole being and transform me into a faithful disciple of Christ.

Amen.

God's Word strikes the heart. What word or phrase touched your heart?

_____

_____

_____

_____

Each year Joseph and Mary faithfully journeyed to Jerusalem for the feast of the Passover. Since Jesus was twelve years old, He went with them. How do you think Mary and Joseph felt when Jesus was lost for three days?

_____

_____

_____

_____

Where was Jesus when they found him? What was He doing?

_____

_____

_____

_____

TODAY'S DATE _____

Jesus returned to Nazareth with Mary and Joseph. What does Jesus teach you in His willingness to obey?

_____

_____

_____

_____

Mary kept these things in her heart. Do you ever struggle to understand God's plan for you? Ask this question in prayer: "Lord, how can I learn to accept Your will when it is hard to understand? What virtues do I need to cultivate (see pages 323-326)?" Write down what He says.

_____

_____

_____

_____

_____

Think about a time when you struggled to listen to and obey those people with rightful authority. Write down the reasons it is difficult for you to listen and/or obey at times.

_____

_____

_____

_____

_____

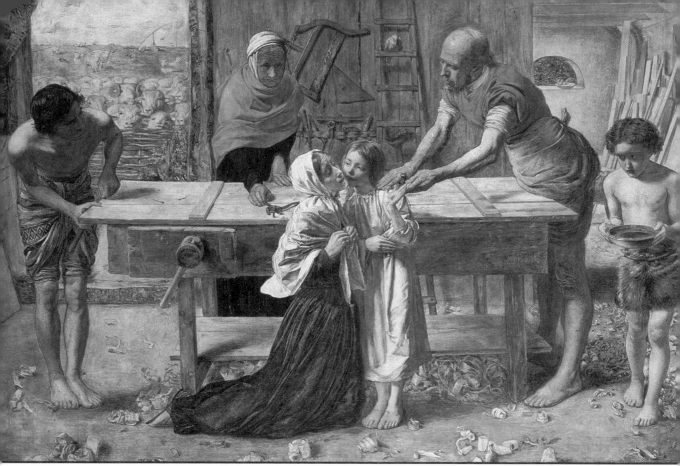

Christ in the House of His Parents, Millais, J.E. & Solomon, Rebecca / Private Collection / Bridgeman Images

Silently study the painting. Look at the setting and details. How does the artist depict the Holy Family? Who is the boy at the far right?

_____

_____

_____

Look at the painting's central action. What has happened to Jesus? Look at the expression on the faces of Jesus and Mary. Who appears to be suffering more and why?

_____

_____

_____

How is this scene a foreshadowing?

_____

_____

✝ My Meditation

_____
_____
_____
_____
_____
_____
_____
_____
_____
_____
_____
_____
_____
_____
_____
_____
_____
_____
_____
_____

With Gratitude I Praise You, God, for

_____
_____
_____

— Jesus' Baptism —

Father, anoint me with Your Holy Spirit so that as I read Your Eternal Word, it may penetrate my whole being and transform me into a faithful disciple of Christ.

Amen.

God's Word strikes the heart. What word or phrase touched your heart?

_____

_____

_____

_____

How did John prepare the people to receive Jesus? What did his baptism represent?

_____

_____

_____

_____

Describe what happened when Jesus is baptized. How do you think the people reacted? How would you have reacted if you heard God's voice?

_____

_____

_____

_____

John the Baptist practiced penance and lived in the desert to prepare for the coming of the Messiah. How did his life reflect one who lives the virtues of temperance and hope?

_____

_____

_____

_____

"Jesus, John the Baptist recognized Your presence in His mother's womb and when He met You in the desert. How can I recognize Your presence more in my life?" Write down what you hear Him say.

_____

_____

_____

_____

_____

_____

John the Baptist lived a life of sacrifice and kept his heart pure. Therefore, he was able to proclaim the presence of Jesus and humbly say, "One mightier than I is coming after me." Write down ways you need to practice sacrifice to recognize Christ's presence.

_____

_____

_____

_____

_____

Silently study the painting. Who is present. What is taking place?

_____

_____

_____

How does the artist, Tintoretto, draw your attention to the baptism of Christ? Why is John the Baptist placed in the shadow?

_____

_____

_____

_____

What is the source of the light? How is this significant to the painting's subject?

_____

_____

_____

_____

_____

_____

_____

_____

_____

_____

The Baptism of Christ, Tintoretto, Jacopo Robusti / S. Silvestro, Venice, Italy / Bridgeman Images

✝ My Meditation

_____

_____

_____

_____

_____

_____

_____

_____

_____

_____

_____

_____

_____

_____

_____

_____

_____

_____

_____

_____

🙌 With Gratitude I Praise You, God, for

_____

_____

_____

— John Points Out Christ;
the First Disciples —

Father, anoint me with Your Holy Spirit so that as I read Your
Eternal Word, it may penetrate my whole being and transform me
into a faithful disciple of Christ.

Amen.

God's Word strikes the heart. What word or phrase touched your heart?

_____

_____

_____

_____

Describe the words and actions of John the Baptist when he saw Jesus coming toward him.

_____

_____

_____

_____

Read Luke 1:76–77. How was the prophesy of John's father, Zechariah, fulfilled?

_____

_____

_____

_____

Andrew, Peter, John, Philip, and Nathaniel encountered Jesus, the Messiah. How did they respond to Jesus? How was Nathaniel's reaction different from the others?

_____

_____

_____

_____

"Jesus, Messiah, You call the disciples by name to follow You. How can I hear You speak to me and know if You are calling?" Write down what you hear as you listen to Him speaking to you.

_____

_____

_____

_____

_____

Philip told Nathaniel about Jesus. Jesus said that Nathaniel was a true Israelite and a person without duplicity. If you were to encounter Jesus today, would He be able to say that you are a true disciple without duplicity of life? Write down what virtues you need to cultivate so you are not two-faced or a hypocrite (see pages 323–326).

_____

_____

_____

_____

The Calling of St. Peter and St. Andrew, Cortona, Pietro da (Berrettini) / Fitzwilliam Museum, University of Cambridge, UK / Bridgeman Images

Silently study the painting. Who is present? Where are they?

_____

_____

Look carefully at the sky and describe the contrast you see. How might it be connected to the painting's subject?

_____

_____

_____

_____

How does the artist show the apostles response to Jesus' call, "Come, follow me"? What emotion does this stir in your heart?

_____

_____

_____

_____

 # My Meditation

_____

_____

_____

_____

_____

_____

_____

_____

_____

_____

_____

_____

_____

_____

_____

_____

_____

_____

_____

_____

_____

_____

 With Gratitude I Praise You, God, for

_____

_____

_____

— Call of the First Apostles —

Father, anoint me with Your Holy Spirit so that as I read Your Eternal Word, it may penetrate my whole being and transform me into a faithful disciple of Christ.

Amen.

God's Word strikes the heart. What word or phrase touched your heart?

_____

_____

_____

_____

When Jesus called them, how did the Apostles respond? What do you think they saw in Jesus?

_____

_____

_____

_____

Zebedee was left behind in the boat. How do you think he felt when both his sons left to follow Jesus?

_____

_____

_____

_____

MARK 1:16-20

What did Jesus mean when He said, "Come after me and I will make you fishers of men"? Do you think Simon (Peter) and Andrew understood His words?

_____

_____

_____

_____

Ask yourself this question in prayer: "Jesus, what in my life are You calling me to leave behind? What is preventing me from saying yes to the Father's will?" Write down what you hear Him saying to you.

_____

_____

_____

_____

_____

_____

Peter, Andrew, James, and John promptly responded to Jesus' call to follow Him. Their response was virtuous and required sacrifice. How would you describe them?

_____

_____

_____

_____

Silently study the painting. Who is present? Where are they located?

_____

_____

_____

How does the artist capture James' and John's response to Jesus' call? Think about the image's movement and expression.

_____

_____

_____

The Calling of St. James and St. John, Illustration for *The Life of Christ*, Tissot, James Jacques Joseph / Brooklyn Museum of Art, New York, USA / Bridgeman Images

✝ My Meditation

_____

_____

_____

_____

_____

_____

_____

_____

_____

_____

_____

_____

_____

_____

_____

_____

_____

_____

_____

_____

_____

_____

🙌 With Gratitude I Praise You, God, for

_____

_____

_____

— Marriage at Cana —

Father, anoint me with Your Holy Spirit so that as I read Your Eternal Word, it may penetrate my whole being and transform me into a faithful disciple of Christ.

Amen.

God's Word strikes the heart. What word or phrase touched your heart?

_____

_____

_____

_____

Mary was present at the wedding at Cana. What was her role in Jesus' first miracle?

_____

_____

_____

_____

Jesus said to Mary, "Woman, how does your concern affect me? My hour has not yet come." What was Jesus referring to when He says "my hour"?

_____

_____

_____

_____

This was the first act of Jesus' public life, his "first sign." How did the disciples respond to this sign?

_____

_____

_____

_____

Mary told the servants, "Do whatever he tells you." Ask this question in prayer: "Jesus, what am I supposed to learn from watching Mary in this scene?" Write down what you hear Him saying.

_____

_____

_____

_____

_____

_____

Magnificence is doing great things for God.

The six stone jars held twenty to thirty gallons of water. When Jesus performed a miracle, He provided an over-abundance of wine, bread, and fish. This symbolizes His love and grace which is poured forth abundantly from His heart. Ask yourself how you can live as His disciple by cultivating the virtue of magnificence. What is one way you can use your talent for good?

_____

_____

_____

_____

The Marriage Feast at Cana (fresco), Giotto di Bondone / Scrovegni (Arena) Chapel, Padua, Italy / Bridgeman Images

Silently study the painting. Who is present? Which moment at the marriage feast is shown?

_____

_____

Jesus is not placed centrally in the painting, yet His presence still governs the scene. Why do you think the artist did this? What does His gesture mean?

_____

_____

_____

_____

Look at the figure of Mary. What does her gesture and expression say about her role in the scene and in our salvation history?

_____

_____

_____

✝ My Meditation

_____
_____
_____
_____
_____
_____
_____
_____
_____
_____
_____
_____
_____
_____
_____
_____
_____
_____
_____

🙌 With Gratitude I Praise You, God, for

_____
_____
_____

— The Temptations of Christ —

Father, anoint me with Your Holy Spirit so that as I read Your
Eternal Word, it may penetrate my whole being and transform me
into a faithful disciple of Christ.
Amen.

God's Word strikes the heart. What word or phrase touched your heart?

_____

_____

_____

_____

Jesus had been fasting for forty days and forty nights. He was hungry. Describe each temptation and Jesus' response.

Temptations	Jesus' Response

What do you notice about Jesus' answer to the devil? How can you imitate Jesus when you are tempted?

_____

_____

_____

_____

"Jesus, after the fierce temptation by the devil in the desert, the angels came to minister to You. You resisted the devil's clever words and lies. What are You teaching me and how can I resist the devil's temptations?" Write down what you hear Jesus saying.

_____

_____

_____

_____

_____

_____

Jesus uses the words from Scripture to resist the devil's temptations. Reflect upon your own knowledge of the Bible and how God's Word enables you to live as a disciple. Select a Bible verse you can memorize when you are tempted by the devil. Write it down.

_____

_____

_____

_____

_____

Silently study the painting. Who is present and where are they? Describe the setting.

_____

_____

Which temptation is the artist depicting? What do the colors white and black represent? How do they show the contrast between Christ and the devil?

_____

_____

_____

_____

The devil is shown as dark and yet transparent. How does this represent his ability to deceive?

_____

_____

Christ Borne Up unto a Pinnacle of the Temple, illustration for _The Life of Christ_, Tissot, James Jacques Joseph / Brooklyn Museum of Art, New York, USA / Bridgeman Images

✝ My Meditation

_____
_____
_____
_____
_____
_____
_____
_____
_____
_____
_____
_____
_____
_____
_____
_____
_____
_____
_____

🙌 With Gratitude I Praise You, God, for

_____
_____
_____

— Jesus Goes to Jerusalem for the Passover —

Father, anoint me with Your Holy Spirit so that as I read Your Eternal Word, it may penetrate my whole being and transform me into a faithful disciple of Christ.

Amen.

God's Word strikes the heart. What word or phrase touched your heart?

_____

_____

_____

_____

Jesus went up to Jerusalem for Passover and entered the temple. Describe what He did there.

_____

_____

_____

_____

The disciples recalled the words from Scripture, "Zeal for your house will consume me" (Psalm 69:9). How do Jesus' actions show His zeal for His Father's house?

_____

_____

_____

_____

When did the disciples understand Jesus' answer, "Destroy this sanctuary, and in three days I will raise it up"?

_____

_____

_____

_____

Our bodies are temples of the Holy Spirit. Ask Jesus this question in prayer: "Is there anything in my heart that needs to be 'turned over' and driven out'?" Write a prayer to Jesus asking Him to cleanse your heart.

_____

_____

_____

_____

_____

_____

You are created in God's image and likeness, and sin distorts this image. Look at the painting on the following page. Is Jesus' anger shown toward the people or the sins they had committed? Explain.

_____

_____

_____

_____

_____

Silently study the picture. Who is present and where are they? Compare and contrast the actions on the left side to those on the right.

_____

_____

_____

The relief in the upper left-hand corner shows Adam and Eve's ejection from the Garden of Eden. How does the scene relate to Christ driving out the traders from the temple?

_____

_____

_____

How does the artist, El Greco, depict the sinfulness of Adam and Eve and the traders in the temple? How does he depict their reaction to their sins?

_____

_____

_____

Christ Driving the Traders from the Temple, Greco, El (Domenico Theotocopuli) / National Gallery, London, UK / Bridgeman Images

✝ My Meditation

_____

_____

_____

_____

_____

_____

_____

_____

_____

_____

_____

_____

_____

_____

_____

_____

_____

_____

_____

_____

🙌 With Gratitude I Praise You, God, for

_____

_____

_____

JOHN 3:1-21

— Jesus and Nicodemus —

Father, anoint me with Your Holy Spirit so that as I read Your Eternal Word, it may penetrate my whole being and transform me into a faithful disciple of Christ.

Amen.

God's Word strikes the heart. What word or phrase touched your heart?

_____

_____

_____

_____

Who did Nicodemus believe Jesus was? Why do you think he came to Jesus at night?

_____

_____

_____

_____

John the Baptist said, "I have baptized you with water; he will baptize you with the Holy Spirit" (Mark 1:8). Jesus tells Nicodemus that no one can enter the kingdom of God without being born of water and Spirit. What do you think Jesus is teaching about the necessity of baptism and eternal life?

_____

_____

_____

_____

Read John 19:39–40. How does Nicodemus show that he believes in Jesus Christ?

_____

_____

_____

_____

Re-read verses 16 and 17. Ask this question in prayer: "Lord, how can I be convicted of Your love for me and be a witness to others?" Write down what You hear him saying to you.

_____

_____

_____

_____

_____

Nicodemus had a docile heart and a courageous spirit. He was willing to listen to Jesus' teachings and had the courage to live in the truth and walk in the light (John 3:21). Reflect upon your relationship with Jesus. Do you have a docile heart and a courageous spirit?

Silently study the image. Who is present and what is the primary action?

_____

_____

Re-read John 3:18–21. Look carefully at Nicodemus. What elements does the artist use to symbolize how Nicodemus gradually came to believe? Look at the lighting and other details.

_____

_____

_____

Christ Instructing Nicodemus, Jordaens, Jacob / Musee des Beaux-Arts, Tournai, Belgium / Bridgeman Images

In the painting Nicodemus is fixed on the figure of Christ. To be a disciple of Christ, why must our eyes be focused on Jesus?

_____

_____

_____

_____

_____

_____

_____

_____

_____

✝ My Meditation

_____

_____

_____

_____

_____

_____

_____

_____

_____

_____

_____

_____

_____

_____

_____

_____

_____

_____

_____

_____

🙌 With Gratitude I Praise You, God, for

_____

_____

_____

_____

— Jesus in Capernaum —

Father, anoint me with Your Holy Spirit so that as I read Your
Eternal Word, it may penetrate my whole being and transform me
into a faithful disciple of Christ.
Amen.

God's Word strikes the heart. What word or phrase touched your heart?

_____

_____

_____

Who did the demon say Jesus was? How did Jesus react and what does this reveal about God's power?

_____

_____

_____

_____

How do you know that the apostles believed Jesus could heal Simon's mother-in-law?

_____

_____

_____

What virtue do you recognize in Simon's mother-in-law? Why?

_____

_____

_____

After Jesus spent days working miracles — curing the sick and expelling demons — what did He do?

_____

_____

_____

_____

Ask yourself this question in prayer: "Jesus, how do I know when I need to take time away and spend it in silent prayer?" Write down what you hear Him saying to you.

_____

_____

_____

_____

_____

The virtues of generosity and prayerfulness are manifested in this gospel reading. How can you practice these virtues today (see pages 323-326)?

_____

_____

_____

_____

_____

Jesus healing Peter's mother-in-law, Goul, Philippos / Church of St. Mamas, Louvaras, Cyprus / Sonia Halliday Photographs / Bridgeman Images

Silently study the painting. Who is present? Who is central in the painting? What is Jesus holding in His left hand?

_____

_____

How does the artist show that Jesus is healing Peter's mother-in-law? Describe the expressions and gestures of Peter and Jesus. (Peter is between his mother-in-law and Christ.)

_____

_____

_____

The disciples had witnessed Jesus curing the man possessed by an unclean spirit. Look carefully at their facial expressions. What do you think they are experiencing as they witness this second healing?

_____

_____

_____

✝ My Meditation

_____

_____

_____

_____

_____

_____

_____

_____

_____

_____

_____

_____

_____

_____

_____

_____

_____

_____

_____

🙏 With Gratitude I Praise You, God, for

_____

_____

_____

— Jesus Preaches in the Synagogue at Nazareth —

Father, anoint me with Your Holy Spirit so that as I read Your Eternal Word, it may penetrate my whole being and transform me into a faithful disciple of Christ.

Amen.

God's Word strikes the heart. What word or phrase touched your heart?

_____

_____

_____

_____

Jesus returned to His hometown of Nazareth after traveling in the region of Capernaum. He entered the synagogue and read from the scroll of the prophet Isaiah. How was this passage fulfilled in Jesus?

_____

_____

_____

_____

Why did the people of Nazareth reject Jesus' teaching? How did they react? How was their response different from those in Capernaum (see Mark 1:21–22)?

_____

_____

_____

_____

LUKE 4:14-30

Placing yourself in this scene, how you would have reacted?

_____

_____

_____

_____

Ask Jesus this question in prayer: "Is there an area in my life where I am blind or held captive? Show me how I need to change." Write down what He says to you.

_____

_____

_____

_____

_____

_____

 Jesus was rejected by the people in His hometown of Nazareth. He, too, experienced rejection but persevered in doing the Father's will. Ask Jesus to be with you during times of rejection and pray for perseverance.

Say the Prayer for Perseverance

Dear Jesus,
You carried Your cross to Calvary even though You were
tired, weak, and hurting. Please give me strength not to give up
when life gets hard. Help me keep my eyes on You and Your Kingdom,
so I can do what is right even when I am tired and afraid.

Christ Escapes the Pharisees, Overbeck, Friedrich / Koninklijk Museum voor Schone Kunsten, Antwerp, Belgium / © Lukas – Art in Flanders VZW / Photo: Hugo Maertens / Bridgeman Images

Silently study the painting. Who is present? How does the artist draw your attention to Christ?

_____

_____

Describe the expressions and gestures of the Pharisees and people of Nazareth. What is the crowd's overall feeling toward Christ?

_____

_____

_____

The Gospel states, "But he passed through the midst of them and went away." How does the artist depict this action of Jesus? What does it reveal about Jesus?

_____

_____

_____

✝ My Meditation

_____
_____
_____
_____
_____
_____
_____
_____
_____
_____
_____
_____
_____
_____
_____
_____
_____
_____

🙌 With Gratitude I Praise You, God, for

_____
_____
_____
_____

— Jesus Heals the Leper —

*Father, anoint me with Your Holy Spirit so that as I read Your
Eternal Word, it may penetrate my whole being and transform me
into a faithful disciple of Christ.*
Amen.

God's Word strikes the heart. What word or phrase touched your heart?

_____

_____

_____

_____

Jesus healed the leper and asked him to remain silent. Why do you think He asked him to tell no one?

_____

_____

_____

_____

The leper had to live in seclusion. How did Jesus show mercy to him by his words and actions?

_____

_____

_____

_____

How did the leper show the virtues of faith and fortitude (courage) (see pages 323-326)?

_____

_____

_____

_____

At times, you may feel isolated from your family and friends. Ask Jesus what He is teaching you in this passage. How does He comfort you?

_____

_____

_____

_____

_____

Sincerity is trustfulness in words and actions. The encounter of the leper with Jesus shows the beauty of sincerity and compassion. Write down ways in which you can be more sincere in your relationship with others.

_____

_____

_____

_____

The Healing of the Leper, Copping, Harold / Private Collection / © Look and Learn / Bridgeman Images

Silently study the painting. Who is present and what is the primary action?

_____

How is the virtue of humility shown in this scene? Think about the painting's details.

_____

_____

_____

Imagine yourself kneeling before Jesus. What would you plead for Him to cure? Is there a "leprosy" in your heart?

_____

_____

_____

✝ My Meditation

_____

_____

_____

_____

_____

_____

_____

_____

_____

_____

_____

_____

_____

_____

_____

_____

_____

_____

_____

_____

🙌 With Gratitude I Praise You, God, for

_____

_____

_____

— Jesus Heals the Paralytic —

*Father, anoint me with Your Holy Spirit so that as I read Your
Eternal Word, it may penetrate my whole being and transform me
into a faithful disciple of Christ.*

Amen.

God's Word strikes the heart. What word or phrase touched your heart?

_____

_____

_____

_____

Describe what the four men did to bring the paralytic to Jesus. What did Jesus see in these men?

_____

_____

_____

_____

Jesus knew their thoughts. How and why did He show that He is the Son of Man?

_____

_____

_____

_____

Why is forgiving sin a greater miracle than healing a paralytic?

_____

_____

_____

_____

The four men show the beauty of friendship because they brought their paralyzed friend to Jesus. Ask Jesus in prayer to show you someone in your life that needs to be carried to Him. Write down what He says to you.

_____

_____

_____

_____

_____

Jesus knew the thoughts of those present. He knows the thoughts you hold deep within your heart. Imagine Him asking you, "Why are you thinking those things in your heart?" What would you say to Him?

_____

_____

_____

_____

_____

The Palsied Man Let Down Through the Roof, illustration for *The Life of Christ,* Tissot, James Jacques Joseph / Brooklyn Museum of Art, New York, USA / Bridgeman Images

Silently study the painting. What Gospel moment does it capture and who are the central figures?

_____

_____

_____

How does the artist draw your attention to Jesus and the paralytic? Think about color, movement, gestures.

_____

_____

_____

How does this painting show the paralytic's deep faith in God?

_____

_____

_____

_____

✝ My Meditation

_____

_____

_____

_____

_____

_____

_____

_____

_____

_____

_____

_____

_____

_____

_____

_____

_____

_____

_____

_____

🙌 With Gratitude I Praise You, God, for

_____

_____

_____

MARK 2:14-22

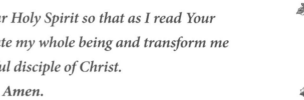

— Jesus Calls Matthew —

Father, anoint me with Your Holy Spirit so that as I read Your Eternal Word, it may penetrate my whole being and transform me into a faithful disciple of Christ.

Amen.

God's Word strikes the heart. What word or phrase touched your heart?

_____

_____

_____

_____

What was unusual about Jesus calling Matthew (Levi) to follow Him?

_____

_____

_____

_____

Generally a tax collector would be looking down to count the money. Why do you think Matthew saw Jesus?

_____

_____

_____

_____

Jesus entered the house of Matthew and ate with his friends – other tax collectors. How did the Pharisees react?

_____

_____

_____

_____

Ask this question in prayer: "Jesus, do I judge others by their external actions? How are You showing me to not judge others?" Write down what you hear Him saying to you.

_____

_____

_____

_____

_____

Matthew, a tax collector, was docile and open to hear the call of Jesus. At times technology enables us to be more present to those not with us as opposed to those in our midst. Jesus speaks to us in the present moment even when we are busy with our work. Make an effort to be present to those with you — unplug in their presence and unplug in your prayer time.

The Conversion of St. Matthew, Tornioli, Niccolo / Musee des Beaux-Arts, Rouen, France / Giraudon / Bridgeman Images

Silently study the painting. Who is present and what Gospel moment is captured?

_____

_____

_____

Find St. Matthew in the painting. Describe the expression on his face. What other details do you notice about him?

_____

_____

_____

_____

Describe Christ's pose and gestures. Then look carefully at the hands of the other men present. How do their gestures show their reaction to Jesus? What might be the significance?

_____

_____

_____

_____

✝ My Meditation

_____
_____
_____
_____
_____
_____
_____
_____
_____
_____
_____
_____
_____
_____
_____
_____
_____
_____
_____

🙌 With Gratitude I Praise You, God, for

_____
_____
_____

— Jesus Heals at the Pool of Bethsaida —

Father, anoint me with Your Holy Spirit so that as I read Your
Eternal Word, it may penetrate my whole being and transform me
into a faithful disciple of Christ.
Amen.

God's Word strikes the heart. What word or phrase touched your heart?

_____

_____

_____

_____

Why do you think Jesus knew how long the man had been at the pool? [Hint: Ann and Joachim, His grandparents, lived near there.]

_____

_____

_____

_____

Jesus asked the man, "Do you want to be well?" What did Jesus tell him to do?

_____

_____

_____

_____

After his healing, Jesus saw him again. What did He say to him?

_____

_____

_____

_____

The man was healed once he picked up his mat. Ask Jesus these questions in prayer: "How can I be healed by willingly accepting my illness or suffering? Is there something in my life which is preventing me from freely walking as your disciple?" Write down what you hear Him saying to you.

_____

_____

_____

_____

_____

_____

After being an invalid for thirty-eight years, it would seem that the man would quickly give up and start to get discouraged. The virtues of hope and perseverance are necessary in times of suffering and illness. Pray for someone who is sick and reach out to them by sending a card or calling them.

Christ at the Pool of Bethesda, Murillo, Bartolome Esteban / National Gallery, London, UK / Bridgeman Images

Silently study the painting. Who is present? Look carefully at the sky.

_____

_____

What detail from the Gospel passage (John 5:4) is the artist depicting?

_____

_____

_____

_____

Look at the lame man, Christ, and the angel in the sky. Is there a visual connection between the three figures? Does this have a symbolic spiritual meaning?

_____

_____

_____

_____

✝ My Meditation

_____
_____
_____
_____
_____
_____
_____
_____
_____
_____
_____
_____
_____
_____
_____
_____
_____
_____
_____

🙌 With Gratitude I Praise You, God, for

_____
_____
_____
_____

MARK 2:23-28

— Jesus Teaching About the Sabbath —

*Father, anoint me with Your Holy Spirit so that as I read Your
Eternal Word, it may penetrate my whole being and transform me
into a faithful disciple of Christ.*

Amen.

God's Word strikes the heart. What word or phrase touched your heart?

_____

_____

_____

_____

What is the purpose of the Sabbath or Sunday rest and worship? Why do we need a
specific day of prayer and recreation?

_____

_____

_____

_____

How does keeping the Sabbath, or Sunday, make us like God the Creator? (Genesis 2:2)

_____

_____

_____

_____

When Jesus claimed to be Lord of the Sabbath, what was He saying about Himself?

_____

_____

_____

_____

Ask this question in prayer: "Jesus, in what way do I need to change in order to keep holy the Sabbath?" Write down what He says to you.

_____

_____

_____

_____

_____

 When, during the persecution of Diocletian, their assemblies were banned with the greatest severity, many were courageous enough to defy the imperial decree and accepted death rather than miss the Sunday Eucharist. This was the case of the martyrs of Abitina, in Proconsular Africa, who replied to their accusers: "Without fear of any kind we have celebrated the Lord''s Supper, because it cannot be missed; that is our law"; "We cannot live without the Lord's Supper."

(*Dies Domini*, 46. St John Paul II)

Would you be willing to die a martyr's death instead of missing the Sunday Eucharist?

Silently study the painting. What is taking place in the foreground and background?

_____

_____

_____

Compare and contrast the Gospel scene in the foreground with the everyday scene of harvest in the background. Is there a connection between them?

_____

_____

_____

What does this painting say about work? What is the role of manual labor in God's creation?

_____

_____

_____

✝ My Meditation

_____

_____

_____

_____

_____

_____

_____

_____

_____

_____

_____

_____

_____

_____

_____

_____

_____

_____

_____

_____

_____

🙌 With Gratitude I Praise You, God, for

_____

_____

_____

— Jesus Cures the Man with the Withered Hand —

Father, anoint me with Your Holy Spirit so that as I read Your Eternal Word, it may penetrate my whole being and transform me into a faithful disciple of Christ.

Amen.

God's Word strikes the heart. What word or phrase touched your heart?

_____

_____

_____

_____

Jesus asked the man with the withered hand to come up and stand before everyone. What virtue did he show by this action?

_____

_____

_____

_____

Despite the Pharisees watching Him carefully, what did Jesus do?

_____

_____

_____

_____

Jesus was grieved and angry by the Pharisee's "hardness of heart." How was Jesus teaching us that anger is not always sinful? Why was His anger not sinful?

_____

_____

_____

_____

Being judgmental can prevent us from seeing God acting in the lives of others. Ask the Holy Spirit in prayer to show you ways that you harshly judge others. Write down what He says to you.

_____

_____

_____

_____

_____

 Humility is an awareness that all one's gifts come from God and appreciation for the gifts of others.

A lack of humility can lead to an attitude like the Pharisees and a hardness of heart. Say the Prayer for Humility that you always see God's goodness and gifts.

 Dear Jesus,

You said, "Learn from Me, for I am meek and humble of heart" (Matthew 11:29). You are God, yet You became little out of love for me. I desire to become little for love of You. Help me to be honest about my strengths and weaknesses. May You be glorified in everything that I do!

The Man with the Withered Hand, illustration from *The Life of Our Lord Jesus Christ*, Tissot, James Jacques Joseph / Brooklyn Museum of Art, New York, USA / Bridgeman Images

Silently study the painting. Who is present? How are Jesus and the man set apart?

_____

_____

Study the faces of the Pharisees. Describe the emotion you sense and contrast it with the man with the withered hand.

_____

_____

_____

_____

How did the man with the withered hand show courage?

_____

_____

_____

✝ My Meditation

_____

_____

_____

_____

_____

_____

_____

_____

_____

_____

_____

_____

_____

_____

_____

_____

_____

_____

_____

🙌 With Gratitude I Praise You, God, for

_____

_____

_____

— Sermon on the Mount —

Father, anoint me with Your Holy Spirit so that as I read Your
Eternal Word, it may penetrate my whole being and transform me
into a faithful disciple of Christ.
Amen.

God's Word strikes the heart. What word or phrase touched your heart?

_____

_____

_____

_____

In Matthew's Gospel, where did Jesus go to give the disciples His teaching on the Beatitudes? Did He sit or stand?

_____

_____

_____

_____

Is there one of the Beatitudes that speaks to your heart?

_____

_____

_____

_____

The Beatitudes teach us how to live as disciples of Christ. What other teaching was given by God on a mountain?

_____

_____

_____

_____

Imagine being present on the mountain listening to Jesus. Ask Jesus in prayer which beatitude you need to live. Write down how you will seek to live it.

_____

_____

_____

_____

_____

"Blessed are the pure of heart, for they shall see God."

	Identify one virtue you can cultivate to help you live as a Disciple of Christ (see pages 323-326)
A Life of Chastity (Temperance)	
A Life of Charity (Love)	
A Life committed to truth and faith	

The Sermon on the Mount, Angelico, Fra (Guido di Pietro) / Museo di San Marco dell'Angelico, Florence, Italy / Bridgeman Images

Silently study the painting. Who is present and where are they? Why does Fra Angelico show only Jesus' closest companions instead of a large crowd?

_____

_____

_____

_____

Why does one of the Apostles have a darkened halo?

_____

_____

Study the expressions and gestures of Christ and His apostles. Describe a time when Jesus spoke directly to your heart.

_____

_____

_____

_____

✝ My Meditation

_____

_____

_____

_____

_____

_____

_____

_____

_____

_____

_____

_____

_____

_____

_____

_____

_____

_____

_____

With Gratitude I Praise You, God, for

_____

_____

_____

_____

— Jesus Responds to the Centurion's Faith —

Father, anoint me with Your Holy Spirit so that as I read Your
Eternal Word, it may penetrate my whole being and transform me
into a faithful disciple of Christ.
Amen.

God's Word strikes the heart. What word or phrase touched your heart?

_____

_____

_____

_____

Why did the elders of the Jews encourage Jesus to heal the centurion's slave?

_____

_____

_____

_____

The centurion was a Roman military office who commanded one hundred men. How was his response to Jesus an example of faith?

_____

_____

_____

_____

What was Jesus' response to the faith of the centurion?

_____

_____

_____

_____

Ask this question in prayer: "Jesus, show me how my faith can increase to believe and trust in Your healing power." Write down what you hear Him say to you.

_____

_____

_____

_____

_____

_____

The centurion replied to Jesus, "I am not worthy to have you enter under my roof." Today how does Jesus enter into your heart? How do you welcome Him?

_____

_____

_____

_____

Jesus and the Centurion, Veronese, (Paolo Caliari) / Prado, Madrid, Spain / Giraudon / Bridgeman Images

Silently study the painting. Who is present? What is the captured Gospel moment?

_____

_____

How does the artist depict the centurion? What does this show about his character?

_____

_____

_____

_____

Look at the followers of Jesus and the centurion. How are they different?

_____

_____

_____

_____

✝ My Meditation

_____

_____

_____

_____

_____

_____

_____

_____

_____

_____

_____

_____

_____

_____

_____

_____

_____

🙌 With Gratitude I Praise You, God, for

_____

_____

_____

— Jesus Raises the Widow's Son —

*Father, anoint me with Your Holy Spirit so that as I read Your
Eternal Word, it may penetrate my whole being and transform me
into a faithful disciple of Christ.*
Amen.

God's Word strikes the heart. What word or phrase touched your heart?

_____

_____

_____

Describe the scene Jesus and His disciples saw as they drew near to the city gate.

_____

_____

_____

How did St. Luke describe Jesus' reaction? What did Jesus say to the boy's mother?

_____

_____

_____

The people began to praise and glorify God when they witnessed the miracle. What type of fear do you think they experienced?

_____

_____

_____

St. Luke was a doctor. How do you think this miracle increased his faith and belief in Jesus?

_____

_____

_____

_____

When you experience sadness, do you feel lonely? Ask Jesus this question in prayer: "When the mother's son had died, You felt pity and compassion. How can I know Your compassion when I am sad? How can I proclaim 'God has visited his people' (Luke 7:16)." Listen to Jesus and write down your thoughts.

_____

_____

_____

_____

_____

Spend a few minutes praying for those who have died as well as for their family and friends. Praying for the dead is a spiritual work of mercy.

Jesus Resurrecting the Son of the Widow of Naim, Bouillon, Pierre / Musee de Tesse, Le Mans, France / Bridgeman Images

Silently study this painting. Who is present? What precise biblical moment is captured?

_____

_____

_____

Describe the difference in Jesus' reaction and those witnessing the boy coming back to life.

_____

_____

_____

How is Jesus' majesty shown?

_____

_____

_____

✝ My Meditation

_____
_____
_____
_____
_____
_____
_____
_____
_____
_____
_____
_____
_____
_____
_____
_____
_____
_____
_____
_____

🙌 With Gratitude I Praise You, God, for

_____
_____
_____

— John the Baptist's Disciples —

Father, anoint me with Your Holy Spirit so that as I read Your Eternal Word, it may penetrate my whole being and transform me into a faithful disciple of Christ.

Amen.

God's Word strikes the heart. What word or phrase touched your heart?

_____

_____

_____

_____

John the Baptist sent two of his disciples to ask Jesus, "Are you the one who is to come, or should we look for another?" (Luke 7:19) How did Jesus answer their question?

_____

_____

_____

_____

Why do you think John the Baptist didn't go to see Jesus?

_____

_____

_____

_____

Jesus described the generation by stating, "We played the flute for you, but you did not dance. We sang a dirge, but you did not weep." Complacency (smugness) and familiarity can settle in our hearts when we fail to recognize the "signs and wonders" of Jesus. What virtues would be a remedy for complacency and familiarity (see pages 323-326)?

_____

_____

_____

_____

John the Baptist believed in Jesus without witnessing His miracles and other signs. Ask Jesus how your faith can be increased to believe in Him without witnessing miracles and signs. Write down what you hear Him say.

_____

_____

_____

_____

John the Baptist's disciples witnessed Jesus performing miracles and teachings, and they believed Him. Write down some miracles and healings you have witnessed in your life. How has this enabled you to believe in Jesus?

_____

_____

_____

_____

Deesis Christ with St. John the Baptist / Haghia Sophia, Istanbul, Turkey / Bridgeman Images

Silently study the painting (This fresco is in the oldest and most revered basilicas in the world). Who is present? Look carefully at Jesus' hand. What is He doing?

_____

_____

_____

Look at John the Baptist. Describe the position of his head. How does this depict John's humility?

_____

_____

_____

In what way is St. John the Baptist an example to us of how to seek God?

_____

_____

_____

✝ My Meditation

_____

_____

_____

_____

_____

_____

_____

_____

_____

_____

_____

_____

_____

_____

_____

_____

_____

_____

🙌 With Gratitude I Praise You, God, for

_____

_____

_____

— The Sinful Woman Forgiven —

Father, anoint me with Your Holy Spirit so that as I read Your Eternal Word, it may penetrate my whole being and transform me into a faithful disciple of Christ.
Amen.

God's Word strikes the heart. What word or phrase touched your heart?

_____

_____

_____

_____

Describe the actions of the sinful woman toward Jesus. Why did she do this?

_____

_____

_____

_____

What was the Pharisee thinking and how does Jesus answer his thoughts?

_____

_____

_____

_____

How would you describe Simon's reaction to the woman? What did Jesus teach him?

_____

_____

_____

_____

Jesus says to Simon, "So I tell you, her many sins have been forgiven, hence she has shown great love. But the one to whom little is forgiven, loves little" (Luke 7:47). Ask Jesus this question in prayer: "How am I judgmental of other people? In what ways can I learn mercy?" Write down what He says to you.

_____

_____

_____

_____

_____

Jesus said, "Come to me all you who labor and burdened and I will give you rest. Take my yoke upon you and learn from me, for I am meek and humble of heart; and you will find rest for your souls. For my yoke is easy, and my burden light" (Matthew 11:28–30).

Sit quietly and reflect upon your life. Surrender your sins and burdens to Him.

The Penitent Magdalen, Tour, Georges de la / Metropolitan Museum of Art, New York, USA / Bridgeman Images

Silently study the picture. Mary looks at the mirror but doesn't see her reflection. What does she see? How does this show her conversion?

_____

_____

_____

If white often symbolizes purity and red is used for sin, what might the artist be saying in the way this women is clothed?

_____

_____

_____

Mary has a skull in her lap. Artists call this "memento mori" — it is a symbol of how we were made for heaven and not the earth and how we are always called to conversion. When have you recognized that the goal is heaven?

_____

_____

_____

✝ My Meditation

_____
_____
_____
_____
_____
_____
_____
_____
_____
_____
_____
_____
_____
_____
_____
_____
_____
_____
_____

🙌 With Gratitude I Praise You, God, for

_____
_____
_____

LUKE 8:1-15

— Parable of the Sower —

*Father, anoint me with Your Holy Spirit so that as I read Your
Eternal Word, it may penetrate my whole being and transform me
into a faithful disciple of Christ.*

Amen.

God's Word strikes the heart. What word or phrase touched your heart?

_____

_____

Who were the women accompanying Jesus and the Apostles?

_____

_____

The disciples asked Jesus the meaning of the parable of the sower. How did Jesus
describe the following:

Seed _____

_____

Rocky
Ground _____

_____

Thorns _____

_____

Rich Soil _____

_____

Take a moment to meditate upon Jesus' teaching. Prayerfully say to Jesus: "Dear Jesus, the seed is Your word. What must I do to cultivate the soil of my heart so it may be rich to receive Your word?" Write down your thoughts.

_____

_____

_____

_____

_____

_____

_____

_____

_____

_____

Jesus describes those who hear the Word of God as having a "generous and good heart, and bear fruit through perseverance." Describe someone you know that has a generous and good heart. How do they persevere?

_____

_____

_____

_____

_____

The Sower, Montfoucault, Pissarro, Camille / Private Collection / Photo © Lefevre Fine Art Ltd., London / Bridgeman Images

Silently study the painting. Who is present? What colors does the artist use? What emotional feel does this give to his work?

_____

_____

_____

How does the artist depict the labor of sowing seeds? Does it seem boring?

_____

_____

_____

Living as a disciple of Christ can seem burdensome and monotonous. How does a good harvest compare to the joy of living in Christ?

_____

_____

_____

✝ My Meditation

_____
_____
_____
_____
_____
_____
_____
_____
_____
_____
_____
_____
_____
_____
_____
_____
_____
_____
_____
_____
_____

🙌 With Gratitude I Praise You, God, for

_____
_____
_____

— Parable of the Lamp —

Father, anoint me with Your Holy Spirit so that as I read Your Eternal Word, it may penetrate my whole being and transform me into a faithful disciple of Christ.

Amen.

God's Word strikes the heart. What word or phrase touched your heart?

_____

_____

_____

_____

In the parable of the lamp, what was the lesson Jesus taught?

_____

_____

_____

_____

Think about a time you used a light in a dark place. How did it expose those things hidden in darkness?

_____

_____

_____

_____

When Jesus was told about His mother and brothers being present, how did He respond? Do you think He was ignoring them?

_____

_____

_____

_____

Ask Jesus this question: "Your mother heard the word of God in her mind and heart. How can I be more open to hearing the Word of God?" Write down what He says to you.

_____

_____

_____

_____

_____

Jesus said, "I am the light of the world" (John 9:5). When we hear the Word of God and act upon it, we are a light to others. What are some ways you can be a light to others?

_____

_____

_____

_____

_____

Light of the World, Hunt, William Holman / Keble College, Oxford,
UK / By kind permission of the Warden and Fellows of Keble
College, Oxford / Bridgeman Images

Silently study the painting. What might be the symbolism between the lantern and Christ's knocking on the door?

_____

_____

_____

_____

_____

_____

_____

_____

Imagine yourself on the other side of the door. How would you respond to Christ's knock and the light He brings?

_____

_____

_____

_____

✝ My Meditation

_____

_____

_____

_____

_____

_____

_____

_____

_____

_____

_____

_____

_____

_____

_____

_____

_____

_____

🙌 With Gratitude I Praise You, God, for

_____

_____

_____

— Jesus Calms the Storm —

Father, anoint me with Your Holy Spirit so that as I read Your Eternal Word, it may penetrate my whole being and transform me into a faithful disciple of Christ.

Amen.

God's Word strikes the heart. What word or phrase touched your heart?

_____

_____

_____

_____

The disciples were fisherman and familiar with the sea. It was not uncommon for a squall to suddenly arise on the sea of Galilee. Why was this situation different?

_____

_____

_____

_____

If you were in the boat and Jesus was asleep, how would you have reacted?

_____

_____

_____

_____

When Jesus awoke, what happened?

_____

_____

_____

_____

"Jesus, the apostles were frightened by the storm and woke you saying, 'Master, Master, we are perishing.' I, too, am afraid of the storms of life. Show me how You will be with me." Write down what He says to you.

_____

_____

_____

_____

_____

_____

During your lifetime, you will experience periods of calm and then suddenly a squall will arise. Write a prayer asking Jesus to increase your faith and recognize His presence in the midst of difficulties.

_____

_____

_____

_____

_____

Christ on the Sea of Galilee, Delacroix, Ferdinand Victor Eugene / Metropolitan Museum of Art, New York, USA / Giraudon / Bridgeman Images

Silently study the painting. Who is present?

_____

_____

_____

What are the apostles doing? What are they concerned with or about?

_____

_____

_____

Contrast Christ with the storm and the apostles' reaction to it.

_____

_____

_____

✝ My Meditation

_____

_____

_____

_____

_____

_____

_____

_____

_____

_____

_____

_____

_____

_____

_____

_____

_____

_____

🙌 With Gratitude I Praise You, God, for

_____

_____

_____

— Jesus Heals the Gerasene Demoniac —

Father, anoint me with Your Holy Spirit so that as I read Your
Eternal Word, it may penetrate my whole being and transform me
into a faithful disciple of Christ.
Amen.

God's Word strikes the heart. What word or phrase touched your heart?

_____

_____

_____

Imagine yourself in the boat with Jesus. Would you have been afraid of the Gerasene demoniac?

_____

_____

_____

How did the Gerasene demoniac react when he saw Jesus? What did he say?

_____

_____

_____

Re-read verses 30–31. Jesus asked him his name. What was significant about his name?

_____

_____

_____

Describe how Jesus showed His power and authority. When the people of the town came to see what happened, where was the man? Did Jesus permit him to follow Him?

_____

_____

_____

_____

Ask Jesus in prayer: "Jesus, in knowing the name of the demons, You manifested power and authority. Help me to know my sins and name them, therefore giving You power to expel them from my heart." Write a short prayer asking the Holy Spirit to convict you of one sin.

_____

_____

_____

_____

_____

The man asked Jesus if he could go with him, but Jesus told him to return to the town and to be a witness. How is it difficult to be a witness for Jesus? What pressure do you experience?

_____

_____

_____

_____

_____

Jesus Driving the Devil From the Possessed, Jordaens, Jacob / Gemaeldegalerie Alte Meister, Kassel, Germany / © Museumslandschaft Hessen Kassel / Ute Brunzel / Bridgeman Images

Silently study the painting. Who is present?

_____

_____

What colors are used in this watercolor study and how are they used to portray the scene's figures and action?

_____

_____

_____

Who is the central figure of the painting? What part of His character is portrayed and what part of His character is most evident?

_____

_____

_____

✝ My Meditation

_____
_____
_____
_____
_____
_____
_____
_____
_____
_____
_____
_____
_____
_____
_____
_____
_____
_____
_____
_____

🙌 With Gratitude I Praise You, God, for

_____
_____
_____

— Jairus' Daughter and the Woman Healed —

Father, anoint me with Your Holy Spirit so that as I read Your Eternal Word, it may penetrate my whole being and transform me into a faithful disciple of Christ.

Amen.

God's Word strikes the heart. What word or phrase touched your heart?

_____

_____

_____

_____

What is faith? Why is it necessary for healing?

_____

_____

_____

_____

_____

Why did Jesus ask, "Who touched me?" Whose faith healed the woman?

_____

_____

_____

_____

Who did Jesus take into house of Jairus? Whose faith healed the daughter?

_____

_____

_____

_____

Ask this question in prayer: "Jesus, You took Peter, James, and John with You into Jairus' house, and they witnessed the healing of his daughter. How can I increase my faith to witness Your healing power?" Write down what you hear Him saying to you.

_____

_____

_____

_____

_____

_____

When the woman touched the hem of Jesus' garment, He knew power had gone out of Him. We are called to extend Jesus' healing power to others by our prayers, presence, and works of mercy. Be generous and reach out to someone in need. List three ways you can reach out to others.

1. _____

2. _____

3. _____

The *Raising of Jairus' Daughter,* Polenov, Vasilij Dmitrievich / Museum of the Academy of Fine Arts, St Petersburg / Bridgeman Images

Silently study the painting. Identify the figures in this scene.

_____

_____

_____

What is the artist emphasizing with the use of light?

_____

_____

_____

Describe the emotions depicted in this painting and then describe the emotions you experience as you look at it.

_____

_____

_____

✝ My Meditation

_____
_____
_____
_____
_____
_____
_____
_____
_____
_____
_____
_____
_____
_____
_____
_____
_____
_____
_____
_____
_____

🙌 With Gratitude I Praise You, God, for

_____
_____
_____

— Mission of the Twelve —

Father, anoint me with Your Holy Spirit so that as I read Your Eternal Word, it may penetrate my whole being and transform me into a faithful disciple of Christ.

Amen.

God's Word strikes the heart. What word or phrase touched your heart?

_____

_____

_____

_____

What specific mission did Jesus give the Apostles?

_____

_____

_____

_____

Jesus instructed them to live simply and not have many possessions. Why is this important for a disciple of Christ?

_____

_____

_____

_____

LUKE 9:1-6

Jesus told them to "shake the dust" from their feet if they are unwelcome. What do you think He meant?

_____

_____

_____

_____

Ask this question in prayer: "Jesus, which virtue do I need to live more fully today?" Write down what He says to you and describe how you will live out this virtue (see pages 323-326).

_____

_____

_____

_____

_____

_____

To be a disciple of Christ, one must know and love the person of Jesus Christ. How has meditating on the life of Christ helped you grow closer to Him?

_____

_____

_____

_____

Jesus among Twelve Apostles, fresco in apse of Church of St Andrew Apostle, Spello, Umbria, Italy / De Agostini Picture Library / C. Sappa / Bridgeman Image

Silently study the painting. Identify the figures. Where is Jesus?

_____

_____

_____

Reread Luke 9:1–6. How does this fresco show the poverty and humility of the Apostles?

_____

_____

_____

How does the artist show the Apostles' unity in Christ?

_____

_____

_____

✝ My Meditation

_____
_____
_____
_____
_____
_____
_____
_____
_____
_____
_____
_____
_____
_____
_____
_____
_____
_____
_____
_____

✝ With Gratitude I Praise You, God, for

_____
_____
_____

— Death of John —

Father, anoint me with Your Holy Spirit so that as I read Your Eternal Word, it may penetrate my whole being and transform me into a faithful disciple of Christ.

Amen.

God's Word strikes the heart. What word or phrase touched your heart?

_____

_____

_____

_____

Why was John imprisoned by Herod? What had John done to offend Herod and Herodius?

_____

_____

_____

_____

Describe Herod's character. What sins and vices were manifested by his conduct?

_____

_____

_____

_____

Jesus said, "I am the way and the truth and the life" (John 14:6). How was John a martyr for truth?

_____

_____

_____

_____

"Jesus, John the Baptist was martyred because of the sins of others. He preceded Your birth and death. In what ways do I need to embrace conversion and repentance to be more faithful to You?" Write down what He says to you.

_____

_____

_____

_____

_____

_____

Fortitude enables one to endure difficulties and pain for the sake of what is good. Identify and write down ways you can cultivate this virtue in your daily life.

_____

_____

_____

_____

_____

Salome with the Head of St. John the Baptist, Luini, Bernardino / Louvre, Paris, France / Peter Willi / Bridgeman Images

Silently study the painting. Identify the figures.

_____

_____

_____

What is the expression we see on St. John the Baptist's face in death?

_____

_____

_____

Look at Salome's face. How could you describe her expression and demeanor? Is it "natural" for a woman?

_____

_____

_____

✝ My Meditation

_____

_____

_____

_____

_____

_____

_____

_____

_____

_____

_____

_____

_____

_____

_____

_____

_____

🙌 With Gratitude I Praise You, God, for

_____

_____

_____

— Feeding the 5,000 —

Father, anoint me with Your Holy Spirit so that as I read Your Eternal Word, it may penetrate my whole being and transform me into a faithful disciple of Christ.

Amen.

God's Word strikes the heart. What word or phrase touched your heart?

_____

_____

_____

Why did Jesus withdraw in a boat to a deserted place? (Hint: Read Matthew 14:3–12.)

_____

_____

_____

How did Jesus react when He saw the crowd of people?

_____

_____

_____

Read Matthew 14:19; 26:26; Luke 24:30. Describe the actions of Jesus in each passage.

_____

_____

_____

How do you know all the people were fed?

_____

_____

_____

_____

"Jesus, You took the fives loaves and two fish and fed the crowd. At times I feel like I
have little to offer to You. Show me what I can give to You so You may multiply my gifts."
Write down what He shows you.

_____

_____

_____

_____

_____

Jesus felt pity when He saw the crowd without food, and He also felt sorrow
when John the Baptist died. Write a prayer as if Jesus were talking to you in
those times when you have felt sadness or were tired.

_____

_____

_____

_____

_____

The Multiplication of the Loaves and Fishes, Lanfranco, Giovanni / National Gallery of Ireland, Dublin, Ireland / Bridgeman Images

Silently study the painting. Who is present? Describe the crowd's gestures and attitude.

_____

_____

_____

Who is Jesus looking at? What message is He giving?

_____

_____

_____

How does this scene foreshadow Holy Communion?

_____

_____

_____

✝ My Meditation

_____
_____
_____
_____
_____
_____
_____
_____
_____
_____
_____
_____
_____
_____
_____
_____
_____
_____
_____

🙌 With Gratitude I Praise You, God, for

_____
_____
_____

— Jesus Walks on Water —

Father, anoint me with Your Holy Spirit so that as I read Your Eternal Word, it may penetrate my whole being and transform me into a faithful disciple of Christ.

Amen.

God's Word strikes the heart. What word or phrase touched your heart?

_____

_____

_____

Jesus and His disciples had just fed 5,000 people. Jesus told the disciples to leave by boat as He dismissed the crowd. What virtue was Jesus teaching by His example?

_____

_____

_____

What detail does St. Matthew offer about the boat (distance) and condition of the sea?

_____

_____

_____

How would you have responded if you saw Jesus walking on the water? What does this reveal about Him?

_____

_____

_____

At what point did Peter sink?

_____

_____

_____

"Jesus, the disciples experienced Your power over creation and responded by offering homage and words of praise — 'Truly you are the Son of God.' I often fail to see Your power in my daily life. Show me Your majesty." Write down what He says to you.

_____

_____

_____

_____

_____

Jesus would often go to a quiet place to pray. Prayerfulness is being still, listening, and being willing to talk to God as a friend. As his disciple, make an effort to schedule time for prayer in your daily life.

Peter Walks on Water, Runge, Philipp Otto / Hamburger Kunsthalle, Hamburg, Germany / Bridgeman Images

Silently study the painting. Who is present? Describe the emotions of those on the boat.

_____

_____

_____

Notice the moon in the sky and it's reflection shining on the water. Describe the contrast between the moon and the other elements in the scene. Can this be related to the figure of Christ?

_____

_____

_____

Describe the expression on Peter's face. How does Jesus respond?

_____

_____

_____

✝ My Meditation

_____
_____
_____
_____
_____
_____
_____
_____
_____
_____
_____
_____
_____
_____
_____
_____
_____
_____
_____

🙌 With Gratitude I Praise You, God, for

_____
_____
_____

— Bread from Heaven —

*Father, anoint me with Your Holy Spirit so that as I read Your
Eternal Word, it may penetrate my whole being and transform me
into a faithful disciple of Christ.*

Amen.

God's Word strikes the heart. What word or phrase touched your heart?

_____

_____

_____

Why did the people initially follow Jesus? What were they seeking?

_____

_____

_____

What did Jesus want the people to seek?

_____

_____

_____

Why do you think Jesus chose to remain with us in the Eucharist? What reality is conveyed by this mystery?

_____

_____

_____

By the end of the Eucharistic discourse, how did the majority of Christ's disciples respond? Who did they think Jesus was? How did the Twelve respond?

_____

_____

_____

_____

Many of Jesus' disciples left after His teaching on the Bread of Life. Imagine standing in front of Jesus after many disciples had left Him. How would you respond to His question, "Do you also want to leave me?"

_____

_____

_____

_____

_____

Faith enables one to know God and all that He has revealed.

Peter responds "Master, to whom shall we go? You have the words of eternal life." Spend a few moments reflecting upon Peter's response. Do you have the same conviction in your heart?

Milano monumental cemetery (photo) / Godong / UIG / Bridgeman Images

Silently study the image. Whose hands are depicted and what are they offering to us?

_____

_____

_____

What is the Bread from Heaven Jesus wants us to desire?

_____

_____

_____

"I am the bread of Life." This image is a close up of a Last Supper monument in the Milano cemetery. How is this a sign of hope for those praying for the deceased?

_____

_____

_____

176   TODAY'S DATE _____

✝ My Meditation

_____

_____

_____

_____

_____

_____

_____

_____

_____

_____

_____

_____

_____

_____

_____

_____

_____

_____

_____

🙌 With Gratitude I Praise You, God, for

_____

_____

_____

— Jesus Cures a Blind Man —

Father, anoint me with Your Holy Spirit so that as I read Your Eternal Word, it may penetrate my whole being and transform me into a faithful disciple of Christ.

Amen.

God's Word strikes the heart. What word or phrase touched your heart?

_____

_____

_____

_____

Describe Jesus' action with the blind man.

_____

_____

_____

_____

The blind man was gradually healed. Why do you think Jesus touched his eyes a second time?

_____

_____

_____

_____

MARK 8:22-26

Once the blind man regained his sight, Jesus told him, "Do not even go into the village." Why do you think He told him this?

_____

_____

_____

_____

Ask this question in prayer: "Jesus, are there places or occasions of sin that I need to be led out of?" Write down what you hear Jesus saying to you.

_____

_____

_____

_____

_____

_____

Blindness of mind arises from lust and prevents us from seeing God. Technology enables you to enter many "villages" of pornography, violent video games, and gossip. Ask yourself this question: "Is there a 'village' I should not enter?" Write down your thoughts.

_____

_____

_____

— Select one way to unplug —

Italy, Campania, Caserta province, Sant'Angelo in Formis, Basilica of San Michele (Saint Michael), right aisle, Stories of New Testament with Miracle fresco, 1072-1078, detail / De Agostini Picture Library / A. Dagli Orti / Bridgeman Images

Silently study the painting. Who is present?

_____

_____

Compare and contrast the figure of Christ and the figure of the blind man. Examine their coloring, attributes, expressions, and gestures.

_____

_____

_____

Describe the blind man's response to Jesus' touch. Can he be an example for us in our own response to Christ? If yes, how so?

_____

_____

_____

✝ My Meditation

_____

_____

_____

_____

_____

_____

_____

_____

_____

_____

_____

_____

_____

_____

_____

_____

_____

🙌 With Gratitude I Praise You, God, for

_____

_____

_____

MATTHEW 16:13-20

— Peter's Confession of Faith —

*Father, anoint me with Your Holy Spirit so that as I read Your
Eternal Word, it may penetrate my whole being and transform me
into a faithful disciple of Christ.*

Amen.

God's Word strikes the heart. What word or phrase touched your heart?

_____

_____

_____

How did the apostles respond to Jesus' question: "Who did people say that the Son of Man was?"

_____

_____

_____

Who did Peter acknowledge Jesus to be? How did Jesus set Peter apart from the other apostles?

_____

_____

_____

Jesus stated: "The gates of the netherworld shall not prevail against it." Why is it important to believe these words spoken by Jesus?

_____

_____

_____

TODAY'S DATE _____

Jesus is asking you, "Who do you say that I am?" Spend a few moments praying and listening to the Holy Spirit. Write what the Father reveals to you.

_____

_____

_____

_____

_____

_____

_____

_____

Jesus entrusted the "keys of the kingdom" to Peter. Pray for those entrusted with leadership in the Church and take a moment to thank them for their service to the Church.

Christ's Charge to Peter (tapestry), Raphael (Raffaello Sanzio of Urbino) / © Belvoir Castle, Leicestershire, UK / Bridgeman Images

Silently study the tapestry. Who is present?

_____

_____

_____

How does the artist, Raphael, show that Peter has been specifically chosen by Christ? How is he different and how is he the same as the other apostles?

_____

_____

_____

Christ gestures toward Peter with His right hand while with His left He points to the flock of sheep, thus connecting them. What might be the suggested connection regarding Peter's role?

_____

_____

_____

✝ My Meditation

_____

_____

_____

_____

_____

_____

_____

_____

_____

_____

_____

_____

_____

_____

_____

_____

_____

_____

🙌 With Gratitude I Praise You, God, for

_____

_____

_____

— The Transfiguration —

Father, anoint me with Your Holy Spirit so that as I read Your Eternal Word, it may penetrate my whole being and transform me into a faithful disciple of Christ.

Amen.

God's Word strikes the heart. What word or phrase touched your heart?

_____

_____

_____

_____

Which apostles did Jesus take with Him? Describe what they witnessed.

_____

_____

_____

_____

Who appeared to the Apostles with Jesus? What was said from the cloud?

_____

_____

_____

_____

Which person of the Trinity is manifested in each of the following:

Voice speaking _____

Cloud overshadowing _____

Transfigured _____

Ask this question in prayer: "Jesus, You were transfigured before Your apostles and revealed Yourself in glory. How can this truth strengthen me during difficult times?" Write down what you hear Him saying to you.

_____

_____

_____

_____

_____

The theological virtue of hope enables one to desire God above all things and to trust Him for personal salvation.

 Pray an Act of Hope

O Lord God, I hope by Your grace for the pardon of all my sins and after life here to gain eternal happiness, because You have promised it, Who are infinitely powerful, faithful, kind, and merciful. In this hope I intend to live and die. Amen.

The Transfiguration, Raphael (Raffaello Sanzio of Urbino) / Vatican Museums and Galleries, Vatican City / De Agostini Picture Library / Bridgeman Images

Silently study the painting. Who present and what is the action?

_____

_____

_____

_____

_____

_____

_____

_____

_____

This painting is separated into two different New Testament scenes: Christ's transfiguration on the top and the miracle of the possessed boy on the bottom. Note how those in the lower scene are pointing to Christ's transfiguration. The artist is deliberately connecting the two separate miracles. What does this visual connection say about the spiritual connection between the two events?

_____

_____

_____

_____

✝ My Meditation

_____
_____
_____
_____
_____
_____
_____
_____
_____
_____
_____
_____
_____
_____
_____
_____
_____
_____
_____
_____
_____
_____

🙌 With Gratitude I Praise You, God, for

_____
_____
_____

— Mission of the Seventy-Two Disciples —

*Father, anoint me with Your Holy Spirit so that as I read Your
Eternal Word, it may penetrate my whole being and transform me
into a faithful disciple of Christ.*
Amen.

God's Word strikes the heart. What word or phrase touched your heart?

_____

_____

_____

Reread verses 1 and 16. What do they tell you about the role of a disciple of Christ?

_____

_____

_____

What does it look like to be a lamb among wolves?

_____

_____

_____

What were Christ's directions to the seventy-two disciples?

_____

_____

_____

What did Jesus mean when He said "the laborers are few"? Was He speaking to this generation? How does this statement apply to future generations?

_____

_____

_____

_____

"Jesus, You said, 'rejoice because your names are written in heaven.' Sometimes it is difficult to be Your disciple. How can I be a more courageous follower?" Write down what He says to you.

_____

_____

_____

_____

_____

Jesus offers praise to the Father for revealing the mysteries to the childlike. Describe the virtue of those who possess a childlike spirit.

_____

_____

_____

_____

TODAY'S DATE_____

The Angelus, Millet, Jean-Francois / Musee d'Orsay, Paris, France / Bridgeman Images

Silently study the painting. Who is present? What kind of people are they? Where are they and what were they doing before pausing to recite the Angelus?

_____

_____

_____

These people work and live on the earth, yet how does the painting connect them to a godly spiritual realm? Note the church steeple in the background.

_____

_____

_____

What might this painting be saying about the manual labor and prayer? Can you relate this to your own life?

_____

_____

_____

✝ My Meditation

_____

_____

_____

_____

_____

_____

_____

_____

_____

_____

_____

_____

_____

_____

_____

_____

_____

_____

_____

🙌 With Gratitude I Praise You, God, for

_____

_____

_____

— The Greatest Commandment;
The Parable of the Good Samaritan —

Father, anoint me with Your Holy Spirit so that as I read Your Eternal Word, it may penetrate my whole being and transform me into a faithful disciple of Christ.

Amen.

God's Word strikes the heart. What word or phrase touched your heart?

_____

_____

_____

How did Jesus respond to the question of the scholar's?

_____

_____

_____

In answering the question: "Who is my neighbor?" Jesus told a parable. Describe the actions of each.

Person: _____

_____

_____

Priest: _____

_____

_____

Levite: _____

_____

_____

What do you think are the two most important lessons to be learned from this parable?

_____

_____

_____

_____

It can be difficult to help a person who doesn't seem to be our neighbor. Ask this question in prayer: "Jesus, how can I be attentive to my neighbors?" Write down what He says to you.

_____

_____

_____

_____

_____

_____

Write down ways you can be of service to others (for example, to your grandparents or an elderly neighbor).

_____

_____

_____

The Good Samaritan, Millet, Jean-Francois / National Museum Wales / Bridgeman Images

Silently study the painting. Who is present?

_____

_____

_____

We cannot see the faces of the Good Samaritan and the man who was robbed, but how else can we discern their emotions? What are these emotions?

_____

_____

_____

Look at the figures and their bodily expressions. What do they say about helping our neighbor? Is it easy? Should we do it regardless?

_____

_____

_____

✝ My Meditation

_____
_____
_____
_____
_____
_____
_____
_____
_____
_____
_____
_____
_____
_____
_____
_____
_____
_____

With Gratitude I Praise You, God, for

_____
_____
_____

— Jesus Visits Martha and Mary —

Father, anoint me with Your Holy Spirit so that as I read Your
Eternal Word, it may penetrate my whole being and transform me
into a faithful disciple of Christ.
Amen.

God's Word strikes the heart. What word or phrase touched your heart?

_____

_____

_____

_____

When Jesus entered the village, who welcomed to Him?

_____

_____

_____

_____

Describe the difference between Martha and Mary.

_____

_____

_____

_____

Jesus encouraged Martha not to be anxious and worried. What was His advice to her?

_____

_____

_____

_____

Ask this question in prayer: "Jesus, how can I maintain a spirit of prayer as I go about my daily work and activities?" Write down what He says to you.

_____

_____

_____

_____

_____

A disciple of Christ is to be a witness to others. How can you share the peace of Christ to others during the course of the day?

_____

_____

_____

_____

Kitchen Scene with Christ in the House of Martha and Mary (detail of food on the Table with Christ, Martha, and Mary in the background), Velazquez, Diego Rodriguez de Silva y / National Gallery, London, UK / Bridgeman Images

Silently study the painting. Who is present?

_____

_____

Examine the figures through the wall opening. Which figure is Mary and which is Martha? How does their depiction relate to their biblical descriptions?

_____

_____

_____

_____

Is there a sense of anxiety or restlessness in the painting? Where does this feeling come from? Is there a calming element in the painting?

_____

_____

_____

_____

✝ My Meditation

_____
_____
_____
_____
_____
_____
_____
_____
_____
_____
_____
_____
_____
_____
_____
_____
_____
_____
_____
_____

🙌 With Gratitude I Praise You, God, for

_____
_____
_____

— Jesus Teaches Us to Pray —

*Father, anoint me with Your Holy Spirit so that as I read Your
Eternal Word, it may penetrate my whole being and transform me
into a faithful disciple of Christ.*

Amen.

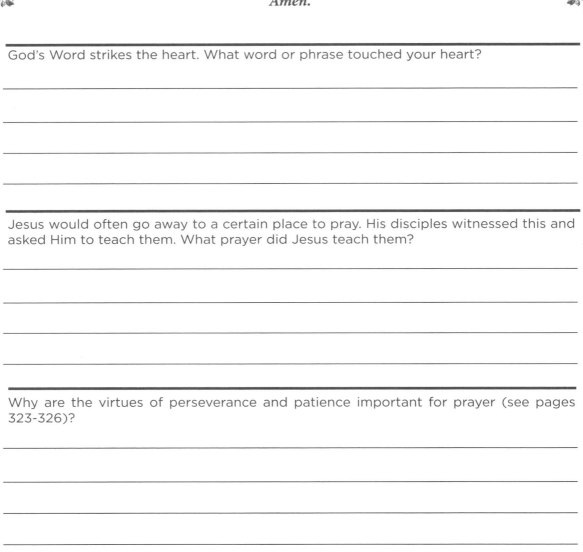

God's Word strikes the heart. What word or phrase touched your heart?

_____

_____

_____

_____

Jesus would often go away to a certain place to pray. His disciples witnessed this and asked Him to teach them. What prayer did Jesus teach them?

_____

_____

_____

_____

Why are the virtues of perseverance and patience important for prayer (see pages 323-326)?

_____

_____

_____

_____

Describe Jesus' teaching on how to pray.

_____

_____

_____

_____

Ask Jesus this question in prayer: "Lord, teach me to pray as You taught Your disciples."
Write down what He tells you.

_____

_____

_____

_____

_____

Recite the Our Father and select one petition you will meditate on for the
week. For example: "Our Father, who art in heaven." Spend the next week
thinking about God, the Father living eternally in heaven. Think about how
He knows the number of hairs on your head (see Luke 12:7).

Christ Teaching, English School (20th century) / Private Collection / © Look and Learn / Bridgeman Images

Silently study the painting. Who is present and what is the primary action?

_____

_____

_____

Closely examine the crowd and the various expressions displayed. Describe them.

_____

_____

_____

As a result of the painting's composition, the viewer is placed into the scene. We are on the ground, sitting behind the figures with their back to us, and we look up to Jesus. Imagine yourself in this position and describe your thoughts and feelings.

_____

_____

_____

✝ My Meditation

_____

_____

_____

_____

_____

_____

_____

_____

_____

_____

_____

_____

_____

_____

_____

_____

_____

_____

_____

🙌 With Gratitude I Praise You, God, for

_____

_____

_____

— Jesus and the Unclean Spirit —

Father, anoint me with Your Holy Spirit so that as I read Your Eternal Word, it may penetrate my whole being and transform me into a faithful disciple of Christ.

Amen.

God's Word strikes the heart. What word or phrase touched your heart?

_____

_____

_____

The crowds witnessed Jesus driving out demons, and yet their faith was weak. How did Jesus show His divinity?

_____

_____

_____

What did Jesus mean by this statement: "Every kingdom divided against itself will be laid waste, and house will fall against house"?

_____

_____

_____

How can living faithfully as a disciple of Christ protect you from the wicked spirits seeking to ruin your soul?

_____

_____

_____

How can you make sure your armor of faith is strong?

_____

_____

_____

_____

Ask Jesus this question in prayer: "Jesus, You have warned us about the power of the evil one. In what ways can I protect myself from him?" Write down what you hear in prayer.

_____

_____

_____

_____

_____

"But if it is by the finger of God that I drive out demons, then the kingdom of God has come upon you" (Luke 11:20).

In the Book of Revelation, Michael and his angels battled against the Dragon (see Revelation 12:7). St. Michael continues to protect us today.

 Say the Prayer to St. Michael to be steadfast in your faith.

St. Michael the Archangel, defend us in battle. Be our protection against the wickedness and snares of the Devil. May God rebuke him, we humbly pray, and do thou, O Prince of the heavenly hosts, by the power of God, cast into hell Satan, and all the evil spirits, who prowl about the world seeking the ruin of souls. Amen.

Christ Casting Out Devils, Brill or Bril, Paul / © The Trustees of the Weston Park Foundation, UK / Bridgeman Images

Silently study the painting. Who is present?

_____

_____

_____

Carefully study the painting's elements and details. Which do you recognize from the depicted Gospel narrative? Is there anything in the scene that is not in the passage? Does this still add meaning to the painting's subject?

_____

_____

_____

_____

_____

My Meditation

_____

_____

_____

_____

_____

_____

_____

_____

_____

_____

_____

_____

_____

_____

_____

_____

_____

_____

_____

With Gratitude I Praise You, God, for

_____

_____

_____

— Jesus Dines with the Pharisee —

Father, anoint me with Your Holy Spirit so that as I read Your
Eternal Word, it may penetrate my whole being and transform me
into a faithful disciple of Christ.
Amen.

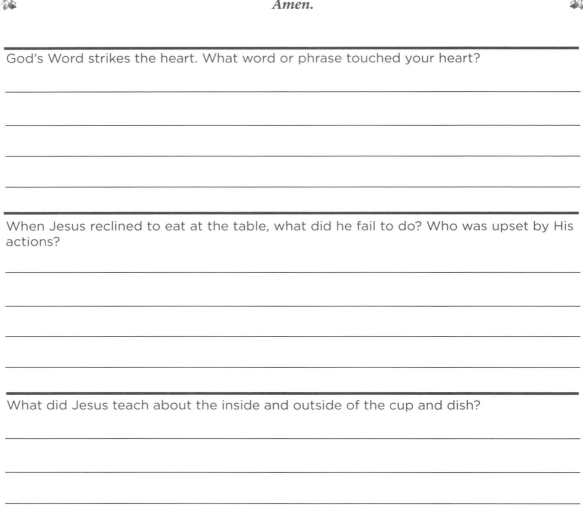

God's Word strikes the heart. What word or phrase touched your heart?

_____

_____

_____

_____

When Jesus reclined to eat at the table, what did he fail to do? Who was upset by His actions?

_____

_____

_____

_____

What did Jesus teach about the inside and outside of the cup and dish?

_____

_____

_____

_____

Why is giving alms a way to cleanse the cup (one's heart/soul)?

_____

_____

_____

_____

Ask this question in prayer: "Jesus, how can I cleanse my heart of self-righteousness so I will not judge others harshly or too quickly?" Write down what you hear Him saying.

_____

_____

_____

_____

_____

Kindness is expressing genuine concern for the well-being of others and anticipating their needs.

Jesus says to cleanse or purify our heart from within, we should give alms. Seek an opportunity to do a corporal work of mercy — feed the hungry, shelter the homeless, clothe the naked, visit the sick, give drink to the thirst.

Jesus Invited to Dinner with the Pharisee, illustration from the Gospel of Saint Luke, Debrie, Gabriel Francois Louis / Private Collection / Prismatic Pictures / Bridgeman Images

Silently study the illustration. Who is present?

_____

_____

_____

Find Christ in the scene. How does the artist help us identify Him?

_____

_____

_____

Compare and contrast the figure of Jesus with that of the Pharisee (the turbaned man in the center). What do their physical features and gestures reveal about their nature?

_____

_____

_____

✝ My Meditation

_____
_____
_____
_____
_____
_____
_____
_____
_____
_____
_____
_____
_____
_____
_____
_____
_____
_____
_____
_____
_____
_____

🙌 With Gratitude I Praise You, God, for

_____
_____
_____

— Courage Under Persecution —

Father, anoint me with Your Holy Spirit so that as I read Your Eternal Word, it may penetrate my whole being and transform me into a faithful disciple of Christ.

Amen.

God's Word strikes the heart. What word or phrase touched your heart?

_____

_____

_____

_____

Jesus warned the crowds about the leaven of the Pharisees. Why was this warning necessary? Think about how leaven affects the dough.

_____

_____

_____

_____

Who did Jesus say we must fear and why?

_____

_____

_____

_____

What did Jesus reveal to us about the Father's love? How does this bring you comfort?

_____

_____

_____

_____

Ask this question in prayer: "Jesus, show me how I can daily acknowledge You before others. How can I live as an authentic and sincere disciple?" Write down what you hear Him saying to you.

_____

_____

_____

_____

_____

 Fortitude enables one to endure difficulties and pain for the sake of what is good.

When others ridicule or tease us, it is difficult to remain faithful to Christ.

Say the Prayer for Fortitude. Ask for the grace to live as a disciple of Christ.

Dear Jesus,
Alone I am weak, but with You I can do all things. Give me
the grace to be strong against temptations and bold in proclaiming You
and Your Church on earth.

The Forerunners of Christ with Saints and Martyrs, Angelico, Fra (Guido di Pietro) / National Gallery, London, UK / Bridgeman Images

Silently study the painting. Who is present? Can you identify any specific figures?

_____

_____

_____

What is the painting's primary coloring and overall tone? What meaning does it give to the scene and the figures?

_____

_____

_____

How can we relate this painting of biblical figures, saints, and martyrs to the passage Luke 12:1–9?

_____

_____

_____

✝ My Meditation

_____
_____
_____
_____
_____
_____
_____
_____
_____
_____
_____
_____
_____
_____
_____
_____
_____
_____
_____
_____

🙌 With Gratitude I Praise You, God, for

_____
_____
_____
_____

LUKE 12:16-34

— Trusting in God's Providence —

Father, anoint me with Your Holy Spirit so that as I read Your Eternal Word, it may penetrate my whole being and transform me into a faithful disciple of Christ.

Amen.

God's Word strikes the heart. What word or phrase touched your heart?

_____

_____

_____

_____

How was the rich man foolish? What are the "riches" that matter to God?

_____

_____

_____

_____

Select two examples of how we can be assured of God's providential care for us.

_____

_____

_____

_____

LUKE 12:16-34

Read verses 21 and 34. Think about the treasures in your life. Is your heart properly ordered?

_____
_____
_____
_____

Ask this question in prayer: "Jesus, You have revealed to us how God the Father provides for His creation. In what ways does He care for me and my life?" Write down what He reveals to you.

_____
_____
_____
_____
_____
_____

 When our heart is anchored in God, we have confidence in His divine providence and seek to store up treasure in heaven. The theological virtue of hope enables one to desire God above all things and to trust Him for personal salvation.

 Pray an Act of Hope

O Lord God, I hope by Your grace for the pardon of all my sins and after life here to gain eternal happiness, because You have promised it, Who are infinitely powerful, faithful, kind, and merciful. In this hope I intend to live and die. Amen.

The Eternal Father, Veronese (Paolo Caliari) / Hospital Tavera, Toledo, Spain / Bridgeman Images

Silently study the painting. How do you sense God's providential care?

_____

_____

God the Father and the Holy Spirit are non-bodily spiritual beings represented by the figure of the Father and the dove. What do these figures in the painting reveal about God's nature?

_____

_____

_____

God the Father and the Holy Spirit make the same gesture. What is the meaning and significance of this gesture?

_____

_____

_____

✝ My Meditation

_____
_____
_____
_____
_____
_____
_____
_____
_____
_____
_____
_____
_____
_____
_____
_____
_____
_____

🙌 With Gratitude I Praise You, God, for

_____
_____
_____

TODAY'S DATE_____

— Parable of the Barren Fig Tree —

Father, anoint me with Your Holy Spirit so that as I read Your Eternal Word, it may penetrate my whole being and transform me into a faithful disciple of Christ.

Amen.

God's Word strikes the heart. What word or phrase touched your heart?

_____

_____

_____

_____

What did Jesus teach about the parable of the barren fig tree? What solution did the gardener offer?

_____

_____

_____

_____

The fig tree was still alive, and yet it wasn't producing fruits. How does this compare to your life in Christ? What are some ways you can cultivate your spiritual life?

_____

_____

_____

_____

Read Galatians 5:19–26.

List the fruit of the Holy Spirit

_____

_____

_____

_____

List the works of flesh of the barren tree

_____

_____

_____

_____

Ask Jesus this question in prayer: "Jesus, am I a barren tree or one that bears fruit? Send Your Holy Spirit to enlighten my mind and heart." Write down what He says to you.

_____

_____

_____

_____

_____

Charity enables one to love as God Himself loves, to love God above all things, and one's neighbor as oneself

Select one way to unplug today to create an interior space of silence so the fruits of the Holy Spirit may be cultivated through prayer and sacrifice.

The Barren Fig Tree, illustration for *The Life of Christ*, Tissot, James Jacques Joseph / Brooklyn Museum of Art, New York, USA / Bridgeman Images

Silently study the painting. Who is present?

_____

_____

The fig tree is one of the painting's primary subjects. It fills most of the canvas. How does the artist depict the tree?

_____

_____

_____

The man to the left of the tree is shown asking for mercy on behalf of the tree. How can we relate to the symbolic figure of the tree?

_____

_____

_____

✝ My Meditation

_____

_____

_____

_____

_____

_____

_____

_____

_____

_____

_____

_____

_____

_____

_____

_____

_____

_____

🙌 With Gratitude I Praise You, God, for

_____

_____

_____

— The Narrow Door —

Father, anoint me with Your Holy Spirit so that as I read Your Eternal Word, it may penetrate my whole being and transform me into a faithful disciple of Christ.

Amen.

God's Word strikes the heart. What word or phrase touched your heart?

_____

_____

_____

_____

How did Jesus' response in verse 24 contradict what people think?

_____

_____

_____

_____

Jesus said the door would not be opened to those knocking. And while they believed they "ate and drank with him," they were not permitted to enter. Why is this teaching important?

_____

_____

_____

_____

How should you live in order to enter through the narrow gate?

_____

_____

_____

_____

"Jesus, Lord and Savior, may I never presume Your mercy. Show me what virtues I need to cultivate in order to enter the narrow gate." Write down what He says to you.

_____

_____

_____

_____

_____

Perseverance is taking the steps necessary to carry out objectives in spite of difficulties.

Jesus said that many won't be strong enough to enter through the narrow gate. Pray for an increase of the virtue of perseverance.

The Importunate Neighbour, Hunt, William Holman / National Gallery of Victoria, Melbourne, Australia / Felton Bequest / Bridgeman Images

Silently study the painting. What is taking place?

_____

_____

_____

Examine the figure of the man. What does his bodily expression reveal about his spiritual and inner state?

_____

_____

_____

The artist of this painting, Hunt, also painted the previously seen painting, *The Light of the World* (page 144). How are these two paintings similar?

_____

_____

_____

✝ My Meditation

_____

_____

_____

_____

_____

_____

_____

_____

_____

_____

_____

_____

_____

_____

_____

_____

_____

_____

_____

_____

_____

🙌 With Gratitude I Praise You, God, for

_____

_____

_____

— Jesus Goes Up to Jerusalem: The Dedication —

Father, anoint me with Your Holy Spirit so that as I read Your Eternal Word, it may penetrate my whole being and transform me into a faithful disciple of Christ.

Amen.

God's Word strikes the heart. What word or phrase touched your heart?

_____

_____

_____

_____

Jesus continued to witness by His words and deeds, but the Jews did not have "ears that hear." Why did they threaten to stone Him or have Him arrested?

_____

_____

_____

_____

When Jesus departed Jerusalem and crossed the Jordan River, how was He received?

_____

_____

_____

_____

Describe the difference between the Jews and those who came to see Jesus.

_____

_____

_____

_____

Ask this question in prayer: "Jesus, those who were baptized by John recognized their sins and repented. How am I in need of repentance so I may seek You more fully?" Write down what He says to you.

_____

_____

_____

_____

_____

_____

 Humility is an awareness that one's gifts come from God and appreciation for the gifts of others.

 Say the Prayer for Humility

Dear Jesus,

You said, "Learn from Me, for I am meek and humble of heart" (Matthew 11:29). You are God, yet You became little out of love for me. I desire to become little for love of You. Help me to be honest about my strengths and weaknesses. May You be glorified in everything that I do!

The Jews took up Stones to Cast at Him, Illustration for *The Life of Christ*, Tissot, James Jacques Joseph / Brooklyn Museum of Art, New York, USA / Bridgeman In

Silently study the painting. Who is present? What is taking place?

_____

_____

_____

Look at the figures in the crowd. What emotions do they exhibit? Compare it to Jesus' expression and gesture.

_____

_____

_____

In the painting, Christ responds to the angry, violent crowd with a blessing, a gesture of forgiveness. When have you experienced God's forgiveness despite your anger or frustration?

_____

_____

_____

✝ My Meditation

_____
_____
_____
_____
_____
_____
_____
_____
_____
_____
_____
_____
_____
_____
_____
_____
_____
_____
_____
_____
_____
_____

🙌 With Gratitude I Praise You, God, for

_____
_____
_____
_____

LUKE 15:1–10

— Parables of the Lost —

*Father, anoint me with Your Holy Spirit so that as I read Your
Eternal Word, it may penetrate my whole being and transform me
into a faithful disciple of Christ.*

Amen.

God's Word strikes the heart. What word or phrase touched your heart?

_____

_____

_____

_____

In the Parable of the Lost Sheep, what word or phrase touched your heart and why?

_____

_____

_____

_____

Why would there be more joy in heaven over the repentance of one sinner as opposed
to ninety-nine righteous who have no need of repentance?

_____

_____

_____

_____

Again Jesus speaks of the angels of God rejoicing over the repentance of one sinner. What does this teach you about God's love and mercy?

_____

_____

_____

_____

"Jesus, You seek me like the woman looking for the one lost coin. Enlighten my mind and heart so I may see any guilt or shame which prevents me from trusting in You." Write down what He says to you.

_____

_____

_____

_____

_____

_____

 Sincerity is trustfulness in words and actions; honesty and enthusiasm toward others.

Unlike the Pharisees and scribes, the tax collectors and sinners received Jesus' message with sincerity. Seek ways to cultivate sincerity by listening to others and responding with honesty in words and actions.

 Say the Prayer for Sincerity

Dear Jesus,

Please give me the grace to be honest in all my words and actions.
When someone is speaking, give me the patience to listen attentively. Amen.

The Lost Sheep, Kykkos Monastery, Troodos Mountains, Cyprus Cypriot / Kykkos Monastery, Troodos Mountains, Cyprus. / Prismatic Pictures / Bridgeman Images

Silently study the mosaic. Describe its overall tone and feeling. Look at the colors, expressions, and other details.

_____

_____

_____

_____

In this scene, the lost sheep is found. Jesus as a shepherd places it across His shoulders. Everything is at peace. What is this scene a metaphor of?

_____

_____

_____

✝ My Meditation

_____

_____

_____

_____

_____

_____

_____

_____

_____

_____

_____

_____

_____

_____

_____

_____

_____

_____

🙌 With Gratitude I Praise You, God, for

_____

_____

_____

— Lazarus and the Rich Man —

Father, anoint me with Your Holy Spirit so that as I read Your Eternal Word, it may penetrate my whole being and transform me into a faithful disciple of Christ.

Amen.

God's Word strikes the heart. What word or phrase touched your heart?

_____

_____

_____

_____

Describe the contrast between Lazarus and the rich man:

Lazarus   _____

_____

_____

Rich Man   _____

_____

_____

When the rich man died, what did he experience?

_____

_____

_____

_____

The dullness of sense arises from the sin of gluttony. In the parable it would seem that the rich man lost a sense of sin and sensitivity to those around him. Why didn't Abraham heed the rich man's request?

_____

_____

_____

_____

Ask Jesus to increase in you the gift of fear and show you how your sins offend Him. Write your response.

_____

_____

_____

_____

_____

Temperance enables one to be moderate in the pleasure and use of created goods.

The virtue of temperance helps us to strike a balance in our lives. Identify one area in your life where you need to strike a balance. For example, do you eat too much junk food and too little healthy food?

 Say the Prayer for Sincerity

Heavenly Father,
You surround me with good things. I ask for the grace to use Your gifts rightly, allowing You to control my desires for the things You put into my life.

Lazarus and the Rich Man's Table (from Luke XVI), Hoecke, Kasper or Gaspar van den / Johnny van Haeften Gallery, London, UK / Bridgeman Images

Silently study the painting. Who is present?

_____

_____

Describe the table, its objects, and those seated at it. How does the artist convey a sense of over-abundance and wealth? How does this scene compare to the scene on the left with Lazarus?

_____

_____

_____

_____

What is occurring in the sky at the upper left portion of the painting? How might this presence be connected to the scene of Lazarus and the rich man's table?

_____

_____

_____

✝ My Meditation

_____

_____

_____

_____

_____

_____

_____

_____

_____

_____

_____

_____

_____

_____

_____

_____

_____

_____

_____

With Gratitude I Praise You, God, for

_____

_____

_____

— Ten Lepers —

Father, anoint me with Your Holy Spirit so that as I read Your Eternal Word, it may penetrate my whole being and transform me into a faithful disciple of Christ.

Amen.

God's Word strikes the heart. What word or phrase touched your heart?

_____

_____

_____

_____

As Jesus journeyed to Jerusalem, He encountered ten lepers. What did He instruct them to do?

_____

_____

_____

_____

The lepers were cured. Describe their response.

_____

_____

_____

_____

Describe the one leper's expression of gratitude.

_____

_____

_____

_____

Every time you ask for forgiveness, Jesus forgives your sins. Ask this question in prayer: "Jesus, when You forgive my sins, do I express my gratitude by glorifying You and seeking to change my life?" Write down what He shows you.

_____

_____

_____

_____

_____

Gratitude is a thankful disposition of mind and heart.

Think of someone you have failed to acknowledge or have failed to express gratitude. Call that person or send them an email or card.

 Say the Prayer for Gratitude

Dear Jesus,
Please give me a thankful heart,
realizing that all I have comes from You.

Jesus with the One Leper Who Returned to Give Thanks, Hole, William Brassey / Private Collection / © Look and Learn / Bridgeman Images

Silently study the painting. Who is present? What is taking place?

_____

_____

_____

Compare and contrast the single figure of the grateful leper to the group of lepers in the background. How are gratitude and ingratitude expressed?

_____

_____

_____

Jesus is clothed in bright white, while the surroundings and other figures are in earth tones. What might be the significance of this?

_____

_____

_____

✝ My Meditation

_____
_____
_____
_____
_____
_____
_____
_____
_____
_____
_____
_____
_____
_____
_____
_____
_____
_____
_____
_____
_____

With Gratitude I Praise You, God, for

_____
_____
_____

— Raising of Lazarus —

Father, anoint me with Your Holy Spirit so that as I read Your Eternal Word, it may penetrate my whole being and transform me into a faithful disciple of Christ.

Amen.

God's Word strikes the heart. What word or phrase touched your heart?

_____

_____

_____

_____

What did St. John reveal about Jesus' friendship with Mary, Martha, and Lazarus?

_____

_____

_____

_____

How long had Lazarus been in the tomb? What was Martha's reaction?

_____

_____

_____

_____

Re-read verses 41–44. Who was Jesus praying to? Was His prayer answered? How?

_____

_____

_____

_____

"Jesus, before You raised Lazarus, You asked Martha to proclaim her faith and believe in You. Show me how my faith in You may be lacking." Write down what He shows you.

_____

_____

_____

_____

_____

_____

Jesus said, "I am the resurrection and the life and whoever believes in me, though he die yet shall he live, and everyone who lives and believes in shall never die."

Write a prayer stating your belief in Jesus and the resurrection of the dead.

_____

_____

_____

The Raising of Lazarus, 14th century, Byzantine (14th century) / Ashmolean
Museum, University of Oxford, UK / Bridgeman Images

Silently study the picture. Who is present? What is taking place?

_____

_____

_____

_____

_____

In raising Lazarus, Jesus reveals that He has power over death. How does the image show Christ's divinity and authority?

_____

_____

_____

_____

Look at the figures of Mary and Martha. What is the meaning of their bodily expressions? Are they an example for us? If so, how?

_____

_____

_____

_____

✝ My Meditation

_____
_____
_____
_____
_____
_____
_____
_____
_____
_____
_____
_____
_____
_____
_____
_____
_____
_____
_____
_____
_____
_____

🙌 With Gratitude I Praise You, God, for

_____
_____
_____

MATTHEW 19:16-30

— Rich Young Man —

*Father, anoint me with Your Holy Spirit so that as I read Your
Eternal Word, it may penetrate my whole being and transform me
into a faithful disciple of Christ.*

Amen.

God's Word strikes the heart. What word or phrase touched your heart?

_____

_____

_____

_____

The rich young man lived and observed the commandments, and yet he asked Jesus,
"What do I still lack?" What did Jesus say to Him?

_____

_____

_____

_____

If the young man was rich, why was he sad?

_____

_____

_____

_____

Why is it hard for a rich man to enter the kingdom of God?

_____

_____

_____

_____

"Jesus, how are You calling me to follow You?" Write down what He says to you.

_____

_____

_____

_____

_____

_____

Moderation is attention to balance in one's life.

Would you be able to pass through the eye of a needle or do you have too many possessions like the rich young man?

Say the Pray for Moderation

Dear Jesus,

Help me to keep a balance in my life, using created things properly and in the right amount that is best for me. I need Your help to set limits for myself in doing things that I enjoy, such as using video games, playing outside, eating, and using my phone and the Internet. Lead me on Your way of happiness!

The Rich Young Man Went Away Sorrowful, illustration from *The Life of Our Lord Jesus Christ*, Tissot, James Jacques Joseph / Brooklyn Museum of Art, New York, USA / Purchased by Public Subscription / Bridgeman Images

Silently study the painting. Who is present? What has taken place?

_____

_____

_____

Examine the rich young man. How does the artist show his sorrowful state?

_____

_____

_____

In the painting, the rich young man is isolated. He is placed at a distance from Christ and His disciples, and he turns his head away to the edge of the scene. What has he done to cut himself off from God and His kingdom?

_____

_____

_____

✝ My Meditation

_____

_____

_____

_____

_____

_____

_____

_____

_____

_____

_____

_____

_____

_____

_____

_____

_____

_____

_____

🙌 With Gratitude I Praise You, God, for

_____

_____

_____

— Jesus Heals Two Blind Men —

Father, anoint me with Your Holy Spirit so that as I read Your Eternal Word, it may penetrate my whole being and transform me into a faithful disciple of Christ.

Amen.

God's Word strikes the heart. What word or phrase touched your heart?

_____

_____

_____

_____

The two blind men were unable to physically see Jesus. How did they know He was passing by?

_____

_____

_____

_____

Describe the actions of the two blind men.

_____

_____

_____

_____

How did Jesus respond when He noticed the blind men?

_____

_____

_____

_____

"Jesus, Son of David, the blind men first saw You with the eyes of faith. How can I be a better witness to the faith when people try to silence me?" Write down what He says to you.

_____

_____

_____

_____

_____

 Faith enables one to know God and all that He has revealed.

 Pray an Act of Faith

O my God, I firmly believe that You are one God in three divine Persons, Father, Son, and Holy Spirit. I believe that Your divine Son became man and died for our sins, and that He will come to judge the living and the dead. I believe these and all the truths which the holy Catholic Church teaches, because in revealing them You can neither deceive nor be deceived. Amen.

Healing of the Blind Man, Greco, El (Domenico Theotocopuli) / Gemaeldegalerie Alte Meister, Dresden, Germany / © Staatliche Kunstsammlungen Dresden / Bridgeman Images

Silently study the painting. Who is present? What is taking place?

_____

_____

_____

Amidst the activity in the scene, Christ and the blind man are a focal point of stillness and contemplation. Reflect on these two figures. How do they demonstrate a spiritual relationship with God?

_____

_____

_____

How does the artist, El Greco, show Christ's tenderness and mercy towards the blind man?

_____

_____

_____

✝ My Meditation

_____

_____

_____

_____

_____

_____

_____

_____

_____

_____

_____

_____

_____

_____

_____

_____

_____

_____

_____

_____

🙌 With Gratitude I Praise You, God, for

_____

_____

_____

LUKE 19:1-10

— Jesus Stays with Zaccheus —

Father, anoint me with Your Holy Spirit so that as I read Your
Eternal Word, it may penetrate my whole being and transform me
into a faithful disciple of Christ.
Amen.

God's Word strikes the heart. What word or phrase touched your heart?

_____

_____

_____

_____

Jesus looked up at Zaccheus and Jesus also looked at the rich young man (see Matthew 19:16–30). What is the difference in their responses? What virtue describes Zaccheus' character (see pages 323-326)?

_____

_____

_____

_____

Why do you think the people of Jericho judged Zaccheus harshly?

_____

_____

_____

_____

LUKE 19:1-10

Imagine Jesus looking at you and saying, "Come down quickly for today I must stay at your house." How would you respond to Him?

_____

_____

_____

_____

"Jesus, as soon as Zacchaeus welcomed you in his home — his heart — he was ready to give away all of his possessions. What must I do to be open and receptive to your invitation?" Write down what He says to you.

_____

_____

_____

_____

_____

Magnificence is doing great things for God.

Zacchaeus opened his heart to Jesus and no longer needed the riches for his happiness. In fact, he freely gave away half his possessions to the poor. Spend a few moments thinking about your possessions. List two items you could give away.

_____

_____

Conversion of Zaccheus, Strozzi, Bernardo / Musee des Beaux-Arts, Nantes, France / Bridgeman Images

Silently study the painting. Who is present? What is taking place?

_____

_____

_____

How does the painting reveal Zacchaeus' humility?

_____

_____

_____

Zaccheus has climbed the tree in order to be closer to Christ, and Christ responds to his desire. How does the painting depict this connection?

_____

_____

_____

✝ My Meditation

_____

_____

_____

_____

_____

_____

_____

_____

_____

_____

_____

_____

_____

_____

_____

_____

_____

_____

_____

_____

🙌 With Gratitude I Praise You, God, for

_____

_____

_____

— Anointing at Bethany —

Father, anoint me with Your Holy Spirit so that as I read Your Eternal Word, it may penetrate my whole being and transform me into a faithful disciple of Christ.

Amen.

God's Word strikes the heart. What word or phrase touched your heart?

_____

_____

_____

_____

Jesus visits His friends, Lazarus, Martha, and Mary. Describe Mary's action.

_____

_____

_____

_____

Describe Judas' action.

_____

_____

_____

_____

What did St. John write about Judas' character?

_____

_____

_____

_____

"Jesus, You cherished friendship and spent time with people You loved. What virtues are necessary for a friendship?" Write down what He says to you.

_____

_____

_____

_____

_____

Do something special for a friend today to show them you love
and appreciate them.

Mary Magdalene Anointing the Feet of Jesus. Bible John 12 / Chromolithograph c1860 / Universal History Archive/UIG / Bridgeman Images

Silently study the print. Who is present? What is taking place?

_____

_____

_____

Identify Judas in the print. What is significant about where he is?

_____

_____

_____

How is Mary Magdalene's position/connection to Christ different from that of the others in the scene?

_____

_____

_____

✝ My Meditation

_____
_____
_____
_____
_____
_____
_____
_____
_____
_____
_____
_____
_____
_____
_____
_____
_____
_____
_____
_____

🙌 With Gratitude I Praise You, God, for

_____
_____
_____

— Jesus' Entry Into Jerusalem —

Father, anoint me with Your Holy Spirit so that as I read Your Eternal Word, it may penetrate my whole being and transform me into a faithful disciple of Christ.

Amen.

God's Word strikes the heart. What word or phrase touched your heart?

_____

_____

_____

_____

Jesus instructed two of His disciples to enter the village. What virtues did the disciples possess that enabled them to respond to Jesus' instructions?

_____

_____

_____

_____

Describe how the people responded to Jesus as He approached the city of Jerusalem. What did the crowd cry out and shout?

_____

_____

_____

_____

When Jesus entered the city of Jerusalem, Matthew described the whole city as "shaken" and asking, "Who is this?" How did this set the tone for the following days in Jerusalem?

_____

_____

_____

_____

"Jesus, Messiah, You were hailed as a prophet as You entered the city of Jerusalem, and yet Your words would quickly be rejected. How can I remain a faithful disciple when those around me call out, 'Who is this?'" Write down what He says to you.

_____

_____

_____

_____

_____

A virtue related to fortitude is constancy. It is strength of soul against difficulties that proceed from obstacles. Daily life presents many obstacles, and it is tempting to give up and go along with the crowd. Reflect upon times you have been confronted by peer pressure. Write down what you should have done differently.

_____

_____

_____

_____

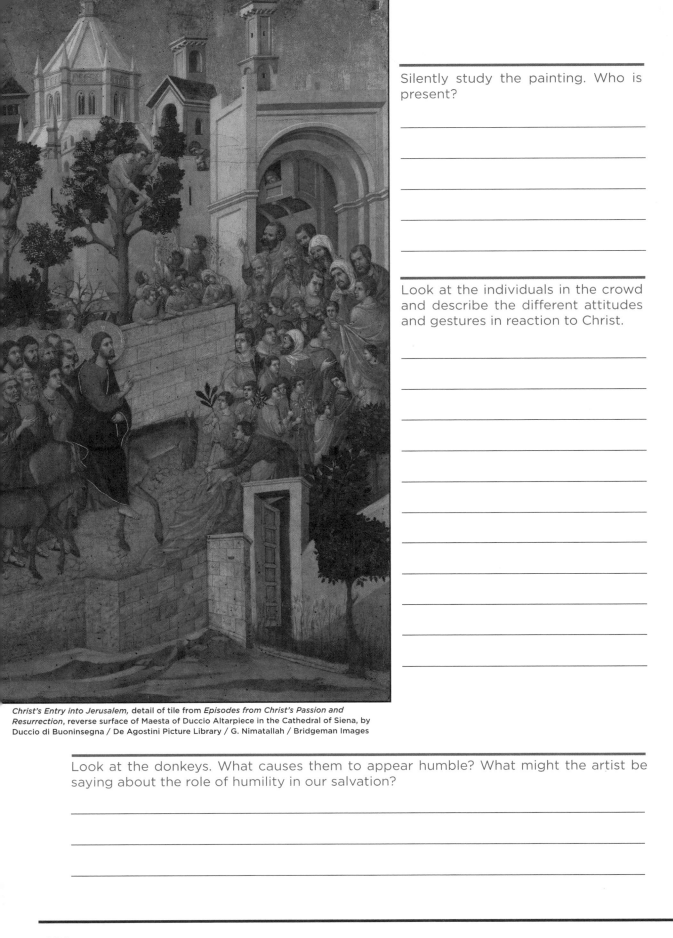

Christ's Entry into Jerusalem, detail of tile from *Episodes from Christ's Passion and Resurrection*, reverse surface of Maesta of Duccio Altarpiece in the Cathedral of Siena, by Duccio di Buoninsegna / De Agostini Picture Library / G. Nimatallah / Bridgeman Images

Silently study the painting. Who is present?

_____

_____

_____

_____

_____

Look at the individuals in the crowd and describe the different attitudes and gestures in reaction to Christ.

_____

_____

_____

_____

_____

_____

_____

_____

_____

_____

_____

_____

Look at the donkeys. What causes them to appear humble? What might the artist be saying about the role of humility in our salvation?

_____

_____

_____

✝ My Meditation

With Gratitude I Praise You, God, for

— The Second Coming —

Father, anoint me with Your Holy Spirit so that as I read Your
Eternal Word, it may penetrate my whole being and transform me
into a faithful disciple of Christ.
Amen.

God's Word strikes the heart. What word or phrase touched your heart?

_____

_____

_____

_____

On the Mount of Olives, Jesus sat and taught His disciples in private. How did He answer their question about the end times?

_____

_____

_____

_____

Read Jesus' teaching about the Good Shepherd in John 10:1–18. What did Jesus teach about the voice of the shepherd? How can this help you when false teachers says "I am the Messiah" (Matthew 24:5)?

_____

_____

_____

_____

MATTHEW 24:1-14

What virtues are necessary for a disciple of Christ to "persevere to the end"?

_____

_____

_____

_____

_____

_____

"Jesus, Good Shepherd, how can I always be attentive to Your voice so false prophets cannot deceive me?" Write down what He says to you.

_____

_____

_____

_____

 To listen to the voice of Jesus requires silence and times when you are unplugged. Make a commitment to unplug to inner silence so you may persevere in living as a disciple of Christ.

— Select one way to unplug —

The Day of Judgment, Martin, John / Private Collection / Bridgeman Images

Silently study the painting. Who is present? What is taking place?

_____

_____

_____

Closely examine the central figure in white riding a white horse. What is this figure holding aloft in its hand? What might this figure symbolize?

_____

_____

_____

This is a scene imagining the end of the world and the last judgment. How does this painting show how all peoples will be judged equally despite their status or nationality?

_____

_____

_____

✝ My Meditation

_____
_____
_____
_____
_____
_____
_____
_____
_____
_____
_____
_____
_____
_____
_____
_____
_____
_____
_____
_____
_____
_____
_____

🙌 With Gratitude I Praise You, God, for

_____
_____
_____

— Parables of the Virgins and Talents —

*Father, anoint me with Your Holy Spirit so that as I read Your
Eternal Word, it may penetrate my whole being and transform me
into a faithful disciple of Christ.*

Amen.

God's Word strikes the heart. What word or phrase touched your heart?

_____

_____

_____

_____

Describe the words and actions of the foolish virgins.

_____

_____

_____

_____

Describe the words and actions of the wise virgins.

_____

_____

_____

_____

The wise virgins' lamps were filled with oil which symbolized how their lives were spent in prayer and acts of love. Why couldn't this be shared with the foolish virgins?

_____

_____

_____

_____

Ask this question in prayer: "Jesus, Bridegroom, You call all of us to the kingdom of heaven, and yet the oil of our hearts must always be burning. Show me how I should live to always have my lamp filled with oil." Write down what He says to you.

_____

_____

_____

_____

_____

_____

Foresight is consideration of the consequences of one's actions; thinking ahead.

The wise and prudent virgins lived in anticipation of the Bridegroom's return and actively kept their lamps filled with oil. What can you do to live in anticipation of Jesus' coming? What is the "oil" that can fill our lamps?

_____

_____

_____

_____

The Wise and Foolish Virgins, Shannon, Charles Haslewood / © Walker Art Gallery, National Museums Liverpool / Bridgeman Images

Silently study the painting. Who is present? What is taking place?

_____

_____

_____

Can you identify which virgins are foolish and which are wise? Explain.

_____

_____

_____

_____

Light is central in this painting. Describe the effect it has on the scene. What do the lamps symbolize?

_____

_____

_____

✟ My Meditation

_____

_____

_____

_____

_____

_____

_____

_____

_____

_____

_____

_____

_____

_____

_____

_____

_____

_____

_____

_____

_____

🙌 With Gratitude I Praise You, God, for

_____

_____

_____

— Conspiracy to Kill Jesus —

Father, anoint me with Your Holy Spirit so that as I read Your Eternal Word, it may penetrate my whole being and transform me into a faithful disciple of Christ.

Amen.

God's Word strikes the heart. What word or phrase touched your heart?

_____

_____

_____

_____

What did Jesus tell His disciples?

_____

_____

_____

_____

As the chief priest and elders discussed with Caiaphas how to arrest Jesus, what seemed to be their primary concern? What does this reveal about them?

_____

_____

_____

_____

Avarice is an inordinate desire for earthly things. It is manifested by treachery, hardness of heart, deliberate betrayal, etc. How is the sin of avarice manifested in Judas?

_____

_____

_____

_____

"Jesus, show me the little ways that I have betrayed You. What virtues do I need to cultivate to be a more faithful disciple?" Write down what He says to you.

_____

_____

_____

_____

_____

Loyalty is accepting the bonds implicit in relationships and defending the virtues upheld by Church, family, and country.

"And from that time on he [Judas] looked for an opportunity to hand him over" (Matthew 26:16). Judas was not loyal to Jesus or the other apostles. Write down ways you should be loyal to your family, friends, school, church, etc.

_____

_____

_____

The High Priests and the Pharisees Propose to Kill Christ (vellum), Italian School, (15th century) / Biblioteca Reale, Turin, Italy / Alinari / Bridgeman Images

Silently study the painting. Who is present? What is taking place?

_____

_____

_____

Examine the figures. Describe their general attitudes and expressions.

_____

_____

_____

Although the illustration depicts a biblical scene, the artist places it during his own time. The fashion and architecture are medieval. Can this scene of conspiracy and betrayal of Christ be placed into our own time? If so, give an example.

_____

_____

_____

✝ My Meditation

_____

_____

_____

_____

_____

_____

_____

_____

_____

_____

_____

_____

_____

_____

_____

_____

_____

_____

🙌 With Gratitude I Praise You, God, for

_____

_____

_____

— The Last Supper —

Father, anoint me with Your Holy Spirit so that as I read Your Eternal Word, it may penetrate my whole being and transform me into a faithful disciple of Christ.

Amen.

God's Word strikes the heart. What word or phrase touched your heart?

_____

_____

_____

_____

"It would be better if this man had never been born" (Matthew 26:24). Why would Jesus make this statement about Judas?

_____

_____

_____

_____

The disciples were gathered for the Passover meal, and it would be their last supper with Jesus. What did Jesus say when he takes the bread and cup? How is the Last Supper remembered today?

_____

_____

_____

_____

Jesus foretold Peter's denial as well as how each of the disciples faith in Him would be shaken. How does Peter respond to Jesus?

_____

_____

_____

_____

"Jesus, the sins and weaknesses of Your disciples are revealed in Judas' betrayal and the foretelling of Peter's denial. How can Your presence in the Holy Eucharist strengthen me to not betray or deny knowing you?" Write down what you hear Him say.

_____

_____

_____

_____

_____

Before Jesus departed to the Mount of Olives with His disciples, they concluded the Passover meal by singing the hymns of thanksgiving found in Psalms 114–118. Read one or more of these psalms as a prayer of thanksgiving for God's gracious love for you.

The Last Supper (fresco), Angelico, Fra (Guido di Pietro) / Museo di San Marco dell'Angelico, Florence, Italy / Bridgeman Images

Silently study the painting. Who is present? What is taking place?

_____

_____

_____

Halos signify a figure's holiness. What might the red cross shape on Christ's halo symbolize? What could Judas' (at the far right) black halo mean?

_____

_____

_____

Describe the apostles' and Mary's (at far left) gestures and demeanor. What do they reveal about the nature/meaning of receiving the Body of Christ?

_____

_____

_____

✝ My Meditation

_____

_____

_____

_____

_____

_____

_____

_____

_____

_____

_____

_____

_____

_____

_____

_____

_____

_____

_____

🙌 With Gratitude I Praise You, God, for

_____

_____

_____

_____

— Gethsemane —

*Father, anoint me with Your Holy Spirit so that as I read Your
Eternal Word, it may penetrate my whole being and transform me
into a faithful disciple of Christ.*

Amen.

God's Word strikes the heart. What word or phrase touched your heart?

_____

_____

_____

_____

Jesus entered the Garden of Gethsemane with His disciples. Imagine being one of the disciples that accompanied Him as He went off to pray. How would you describe the experience?

_____

_____

_____

_____

After praying to His Father, Jesus said, "Your will be done." What prayer did Jesus teach us to pray that includes this same surrender to God's will (see Matthew 6:9–15)? How does living this prayer enable you to live as His disciple?

_____

_____

_____

_____

Describe the arrest of Jesus and identify one particular incident which startled you.

_____

_____

_____

_____

"Jesus, Peter, James, and John witnessed Your transfiguration on Mt. Tabor and Your agony in the Garden of Gethsemane. Their faith was put to the test. Show me how I can be a faithful disciple when my faith is put to the test." Write down what He says to you.

_____

_____

_____

_____

_____

Jesus instructs His disciples to "watch and pray." Silent prayer and spending time with Jesus gives us inner strength to persevere through difficulties. For the next few days, spend time in quiet prayer and think about the words of the Our Father.

Agony in Garden, by Lorenzo Monaco / De Agostini Picture
Library / G. Nimatallah / Bridgeman Images

Silently study the painting. Who is present? What is taking place?

_____

_____

_____

The apostles failed to keep watch with Christ in the Garden of Gethsemane. How does
the painting show the apostles' separation from Christ?

_____

_____

_____

Study the figure of Christ. What do His expression and gestures reveal about His agony
and eventual acceptance of His suffering and death (represented by the cup held by
the angel)?

_____

_____

_____

✝ My Meditation

_____

_____

_____

_____

_____

_____

_____

_____

_____

_____

_____

_____

_____

_____

_____

_____

_____

_____

_____

_____

🙌 With Gratitude I Praise You, God, for

_____

_____

_____

MATTHEW 26:57-75

— Jesus at the House of Caiaphas —

Father, anoint me with Your Holy Spirit so that as I read Your Eternal Word, it may penetrate my whole being and transform me into a faithful disciple of Christ.

Amen.

God's Word strikes the heart. What word or phrase touched your heart?

_____
_____
_____
_____

Judas kissed Jesus, and He was arrested and led away to Caiaphas, the high priest.. Why do you think they were unable to find false testimony against Him?

_____
_____
_____
_____

How did Caiaphas and the other men react to the words spoken by Jesus?

_____
_____
_____
_____

Describe Peter's denial and how he responded when the cock crowed.

_____

_____

_____

_____

"Jesus, You are the Way, the Truth and the Life. Despite the lies and denials of men, You remained steadfast. Show me how I can remain steadfast when surrounded by confusion and falsehood." Write down what you hear Him saying to you.

_____

_____

_____

_____

_____

_____

 Peter wept bitterly when he heard the cock crow as Jesus foretold. To weep for one's sin softens the hardness of one's heart.

 Pray a fervent Act of Contrition for your sins.

Oh my God, I am heartily sorry for having offended Thee. And I detest all my sins because I dread the loss of heaven and the pains of hell. But most of all because they have offended Thee, my God, Who are all good and deserving of all my love. I firmly resolve with the help of Thy grace to confess my sins, to do penance, and to amend my life. Amen.

TODAY'S DATE_____

Peter's Denial, Goul, Philippos / Church of Timios Stavros (Holy Cross) tou Agiasmati, Platanistasa, Cyprus / Sonia Halliday Photographs / Bridgeman Images

Silently study the painting. Who is present?

_____

_____

_____

This painting depicts multiple scenes connected to Peter's denial of Christ. What moments from the Gospel passage do you recognize?

_____

_____

_____

At the upper left corner is a figure caught in the act of covering his face with his hands. Who do you think this person is and what is the significance of this action in relation to the denial of Christ?

_____

_____

_____

✝ My Meditation

_____
_____
_____
_____
_____
_____
_____
_____
_____
_____
_____
_____
_____
_____
_____
_____
_____
_____
_____
_____
_____

🙌 With Gratitude I Praise You, God, for

_____
_____

_____

— Jesus Before Pilate —

Father, anoint me with Your Holy Spirit so that as I read Your
Eternal Word, it may penetrate my whole being and transform me
into a faithful disciple of Christ.
Amen.

God's Word strikes the heart. What word or phrase touched your heart?

_____

_____

_____

Describe Judas' reaction. If he believed in Jesus' mercy, how could he have reacted differently?

_____

_____

_____

Matthew references other dreams that protected the innocence of Jesus (see Matthew 1:20; 2:12, 13, 19, 22). Describe how Joseph responded to his dream.

_____

_____

_____

Pilate's wife also received a message in her dream. How did Pilate's wife respond to her dream? How did Pilate respond?

_____

_____

_____

How have the voices of the crowd changed from Jesus' entry into Jerusalem (see Matthew 21:9)?

_____

_____

_____

Describe how the soldiers treated Jesus.

_____

_____

_____

"Jesus, the noise and confusion created chaos and fear. It can be so easy to be led astray by the crowd and loud voices. Show me how I can stay focused on You when fear and anxiety seem to prevail." Write down what you hear Him say to you.

_____

_____

_____

The chief priests and the elders persuaded the crowds to ask for Barabbas and destroy Jesus. Even in our times, the pressure of society can persuade you to "ask for Barabbas" and reject Jesus. List the virtues you need to be courageous and strong when peer pressure is loud and cries out (see pages 323-326).

_____

_____

_____

TODAY'S DATE _____

295

Ecce Homo, Ciseri, Antonio / Galleria d'Arte Moderna, Florence, Italy / Bridgeman Images

Silently study the painting. Who is present?

This painting depicts the moment when Pilate presents Jesus to the crowd with the words "Ecco Homo," which means "Behold the Man." "Behold" the figure of Christ in the painting. What does His appearance and attitude reveal about His nature?

Examine the two women at the right of the painting. What is their emotional response to what is taking place?

✝ My Meditation

_____

_____

_____

_____

_____

_____

_____

_____

_____

_____

_____

_____

_____

_____

_____

_____

_____

_____

_____

🙌 With Gratitude I Praise You, God, for

_____

_____

_____

— The Crucifixion —

Father, anoint me with Your Holy Spirit so that as I read Your
Eternal Word, it may penetrate my whole being and transform me
into a faithful disciple of Christ.
Amen.

God's Word strikes the heart. What word or phrase touched your heart?

_____

_____

_____

_____

Describe the attitude of the soldiers and those crucified with Jesus.

_____

_____

_____

_____

After Jesus died, the earth quaked and the tombs were opened. How did the centurion respond?

_____

_____

_____

_____

If you were present at the crucifixion, what would have caused you the deepest sorrow?

_____

_____

_____

_____

Spend a few minutes reflecting upon the death of Jesus. Ask Jesus to reveal to you one sin that prevents you from fully knowing His mercy. Write down what you hear Him say.

_____

_____

_____

_____

_____

Look at the image of Christ on the cross and say:

Eternal Father, I offer You the Body and Blood, Soul and Divinity of Your dearly beloved Son, Our Lord Jesus Christ, in atonement for our sins and those of the whole world.

For the sake of His sorrowful passion, have mercy on me and on the whole world. Jesus, I trust in You.

Holy God, Holy Mighty One, Holy Immortal One, Have mercy on us and on the whole world.

Saint Maria Faustina Kowalska
Chaplet of Divine Mercy

Our wounds, those which sin leaves [in] us, are healed only through the Lord['s] wounds, through the wounds of Go[d] made man who humbled himself, wh[o] emptied himself.... The cross is a myster[y,] the mystery of the love of God wh[o] humbles himself, who empties himself.

Where is your sin?... Your sin is there o[n] the cross. Go and look for it there, [in] the wounds of the Lord, and your sin[s] shall be healed, your wounds shall b[e] healed, your sins shall be forgiven. God['s] forgiveness is not a matter of canceling [a] debt we have with him. God forgives u[s] in the wounds of his Son lifted up on th[e] cross.

— Pope Franc[is]

Christ on the Cross, detail from the central crucifixion panel of the Isenheim Altarpiece, Grunewald, Matthias (Mathis Nithart Gothart) / Musee d'Unterlinden, Colmar, France / Bridgeman Images

Describe the painting's overall tone along with its many details.

_____

_____

_____

In the painting, Christ has many small yet deep wounds showing His physical sufferings. What other type of suffering might they be symbolizing?

_____

_____

_____

✝ My Meditation

_____

_____

_____

_____

_____

_____

_____

_____

_____

_____

_____

_____

_____

_____

_____

_____

_____

🙌 With Gratitude I Praise You, God, for

_____

_____

_____

— The Resurrection —

Father, anoint me with Your Holy Spirit so that as I read Your Eternal Word, it may penetrate my whole being and transform me into a faithful disciple of Christ.

Amen.

God's Word strikes the heart. What word or phrase touched your heart?

_____

_____

_____

_____

Mary Magdalene ran and told Simon Peter and John, whom Jesus loved, that the stone was removed. Describe how they responded. Why did John wait for Peter?

_____

_____

_____

_____

Mary returned to the tomb and wept. How did she respond to the angel's question?

_____

_____

_____

_____

When Jesus spoke to Mary, she thought it was the gardener. How did she recognize Jesus? What was her response?

_____

_____

_____

_____

"Jesus, Mary was weeping, and You came to greet her. By calling her name, she was consoled. When I am sad or suffering, how can I know that You also call my name?" Write down what He says to you.

_____

_____

_____

_____

Courtesy is treating other people with respect, recognizing that all are made in God's image and likeness.

Even though John reached the tomb first, he waited for Peter before he entered. John deferred to Peter because he respected his authority and leadership. List three people that you should be courteous to by recognizing their authority and leadership.

_____

_____

The Resurrection, illustration for *The Life of Christ,* Tissot, James Jacques Joseph / Brooklyn Museum of Art, New York, USA / Bridgeman Images

Silently study the painting. Who is present?

_____

_____

_____

_____

_____

What colors and other elements does the artist use to show the heavenly miracle of Christ's resurrection?

_____

_____

_____

_____

Describe the Roman soldier's reaction to Christ's resurrection.

_____

_____

_____

_____

✝ My Meditation

_____

_____

_____

_____

_____

_____

_____

_____

_____

_____

_____

_____

_____

_____

_____

_____

_____

_____

🙌 With Gratitude I Praise You, God, for

_____

_____

_____

— Jesus Appears to Thomas —

*Father, anoint me with Your Holy Spirit so that as I read Your
Eternal Word, it may penetrate my whole being and transform me
into a faithful disciple of Christ.*

Amen.

God's Word strikes the heart. What word or phrase touched your heart?

_____

_____

_____

_____

Describe Jesus' appearance to the disciples. What does He say?

_____

_____

_____

_____

Re-read verses 22 and 23. Jesus breathed on them and gave them an instruction. What
did Jesus' instruction mean?

_____

_____

_____

_____

Thomas was not present at Jesus' first appearance. How does he react when Jesus speaks to him?

_____

_____

_____

_____

"Jesus, You said, "Blessed are those who have not seen and have believed." At times it is hard to believe without seeing. What can I do to increase my belief in You?" Write down what He says to you.

_____

_____

_____

_____

_____

Peace is a fruit of the Holy Spirit and is manifested by interior harmony in the desire of one's heart. When Jesus appears to His disciples, He says, "Peace be with you." Spend a few moments reflecting upon the peace of Christ. Is there something preventing you from experiencing the fruit of the Holy Spirit?

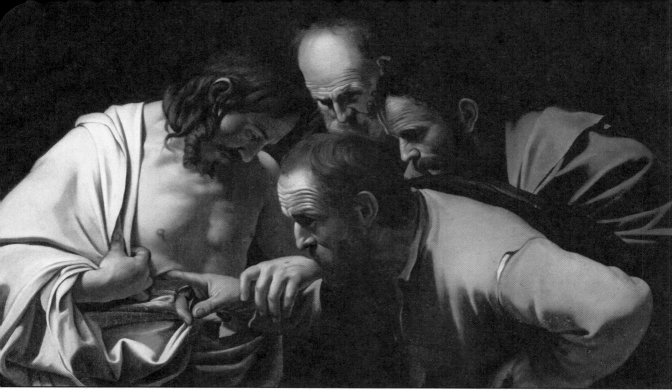

The Incredulity of St. Thomas, Caravaggio, Michelangelo Merisi da / Schloss Sanssouci, Potsdam, Brandenburg, Germany / Bridgeman Images

Silently study the painting. Who is present? What is taking place?

_____

_____

_____

What is the central point of the painting? What are all four of the figures gazing at?

_____

_____

_____

Study Thomas' action and expression. Do you think the painting shows him in a moment of doubt or does he appear to believe in Christ's real presence? Explain.

_____

_____

_____

_____

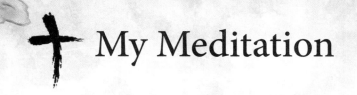 # My Meditation

_____
_____
_____
_____
_____
_____
_____
_____
_____
_____
_____
_____
_____
_____
_____
_____
_____

 With Gratitude I Praise You, God, for

_____
_____
_____

JOHN 21:1-19

— Jesus Appears to His Disciples by the Sea of Tiberius (Galilee) —

Father, anoint me with Your Holy Spirit so that as I read Your Eternal Word, it may penetrate my whole being and transform me into a faithful disciple of Christ.

Amen.

God's Word strikes the heart. What word or phrase touched your heart?

_____

_____

_____

_____

The disciples were at the Sea of Tiberius. Why do you think Peter said, "I am going fishing?" How do you think they felt after catching nothing?

_____

_____

_____

_____

What did Jesus instruct them to do? Who was the first one to recognize Jesus?

_____

_____

_____

_____

After Jesus and the disciples ate breakfast, Jesus spoke directly to Peter. What questions did He ask Peter? What did they counteract?

_____

_____

_____

_____

"Jesus, You came to the seashore to greet Your disciples in their confusion and loneliness. In times of sadness, how can I know Your love and mercy?" Write down what He says to you.

_____

_____

_____

_____

_____

Courtesy is treating other people with respect, recognizing that all are made in God's image and likeness.

John, the disciple whom Jesus loved, was the first to recognize Jesus and stated, "It is the Lord." Just as He let Peter enter the tomb first (see John 20:3-5), He also allowed him to jump in the sea to swim to the shore. John was respectful of Peter's role and leadership among the apostles. Pray for today's youth that they may be respectful and courteous to those entrusted with leadership and service.

Christ at the Sea of Galilee, detail from *Episodes from Christ's Passion and Resurrection*, reverse surface of Maesta' of Duccio Altarpiece in the Cathedral of Siena, by Duccio di Buoninsegna / De Agostini Picture Library / G. Nimatallah / Bridgeman Images

Silently study the painting. Who is present? What is taking place?

_____

_____

_____

Study the hand gestures of Jesus and Peter. What do these gestures express?

_____

_____

_____

Several of the men in the boat are casting a net for fish. What does this symbolize?

_____

_____

_____

✝ My Meditation

_____
_____
_____
_____
_____
_____
_____
_____
_____
_____
_____
_____
_____
_____
_____
_____
_____
_____
_____

🙌 With Gratitude I Praise You, God, for

_____
_____
_____

— The Ascension —

Father, anoint me with Your Holy Spirit so that as I read Your Eternal Word, it may penetrate my whole being and transform me into a faithful disciple of Christ.

Amen.

God's Word strikes the heart. What word or phrase touched your heart?

_____

_____

_____

_____

Jesus instructed the disciples to return to Galilee. When He appeared, what did He command them to do?

_____

_____

_____

_____

What is the formula for baptism that Jesus gave?

_____

_____

_____

_____

In the Acts of the Apostles, what did the two men say to the disciples?

_____

_____

_____

_____

"Jesus, You ascended into heaven and left us to be Your witnesses. In what ways can I be a more faithful witness so others may believe in you?" Write down what He says to you.

_____

_____

_____

_____

_____

_____

As a disciple of Christ, you have been called to spread the faith and teach others all Jesus commanded. Read the Sermon on the Mount (see Matthew 5–7) and select one teaching you will seek to live more fully. Write down the teaching.

_____

_____

_____

_____

The Ascension, Mantegna, Andrea / Galleria degli Uffizi, Florence,
Italy / Bridgeman Images

Silently study the painting. Who is
present? What is taking place?

_____

_____

_____

_____

_____

_____

_____

How does the painting capture the ascent
of Jesus into heaven?

_____

_____

_____

_____

_____

Two realms are depicted, earthly and heavenly, yet they are connected. How do we see
this connection in the painting?

_____

_____

_____

✝ My Meditation

_____
_____
_____
_____
_____
_____
_____
_____
_____
_____
_____
_____
_____
_____
_____
_____
_____

🙌 With Gratitude I Praise You, God, for

_____
_____
_____
_____

ACTS 2:1-13

— The Descent of the Holy Spirit —

*Father, anoint me with Your Holy Spirit so that as I read Your
Eternal Word, it may penetrate my whole being and transform me
into a faithful disciple of Christ.*

Amen.

God's Word strikes the heart. What word or phrase touched your heart?

_____

_____

_____

_____

A symbol of the Holy Spirit is fire. Describe the Holy Spirit's presence at Pentecost.

_____

_____

_____

_____

The gifts of the Holy Spirit are understanding, knowledge, counsel, fortitude, piety, fear of the Lord, and wisdom. How did these gifts and the other gifts of the Holy Spirit strengthen the apostles?

_____

_____

_____

_____

The Holy Spirit's presence united the community; therefore when the disciples spoke in different tongues, everyone present heard them and understood in their own language. Read Genesis 11:1-9. Why did God have to confuse their language?

_____

_____

_____

_____

"Jesus, You promised to send the Holy Spirit after returning to the Father. How can I be more attuned to the promptings of the Holy Spirit in my life?" Write down what He says to you.

_____

_____

_____

_____

_____

_____

Peter and the Apostles were filled with the Holy Spirit and boldly proclaimed the Good News of Jesus Christ. The Acts of the Apostles contains six discourses from Peter and one by Paul. These discourses are called the "Kerygma," which is the Greek word for "proclamation". Read one or more of the discourses to learn how the early apostles preached about Jesus Christ (see Acts 2:14-36; 3:12-26; 4:8-12; 5:29-32; 10:34-43; 13:16-41). How will this help you be a better witness as a disciple of Christ?

_____

_____

_____

Pentecost, Restout, Jean II / Louvre, Paris, France / Bridgeman Images

Silently study the painting. Who is present? What is taking place?

_____

_____

_____

Who is the central figure in the painting? What does this say about that person's role in salvation history?

_____

_____

_____

The descent of the tongues of fire, the Holy Spirit, is shown in a highly dramatized, dynamic manner. What does the scene say about how the Holy Spirit is present in our lives?

_____

_____

_____

✝ My Meditation

_____

_____

_____

_____

_____

_____

_____

_____

_____

_____

_____

_____

_____

_____

_____

_____

_____

_____

_____

_____

_____

🙌 With Gratitude I Praise You, God, for

_____

_____

_____

— *The Goal of the Virtuous Life Is to Become Like God* —
St. Gregory of Nyssa

Imagine a father who also dabbles as an artist. One day he decides to capture the love he has always had for this family by painting a family portrait of his children. Of course he has them all wash up immaculately, put on their finest clothes, and be on their best behavior as he arranges them just right for the painting. Because he loves his sons and daughters so much, this father-artist wants to be sure that the children–models are as perfect as they can be before he captures them forever on canvas.

This imaginary scene is what actually happens with God our Father, and what He wishes to do with each of us. God the Father's perfect Son is of course Jesus Christ. Before even time and space itself, God the Father gazed upon the perfectly beautiful person of the Son. At one point, the Father and the Son and the Holy Spirit decide to capture this love in another way, so they created human persons. The Father makes us who we are after the same pattern He sees in Jesus: we too are made to be kind and loving, we too are made to lay our lives down for other by becoming whatever sort of gift we can be for them, we too are made to become faithful and joyful children of the same Father.

To be a Christian is first to let this picture of Christ be reduplicated in you. All of us should desire this above all things: to become another Christ, to become another Mary. The Father may have only one naturally begotten Son, but He actually desires to have countless children. This is why the Son of God became a man and founded His Catholic Church (see Matthew 16:18). The Church is the place where you and I become children of God, praying to our Father and enjoying the unity of the Holy Spirit. We may not be the Father's naturally born children, but through grace He adopts us as His own sons and daughters. This is what you received at baptism, the Holy Spirit's life in you enabling you to call God Father and friend (Romans 8:15). When you received Holy Communion, Jesus began a new step of slowly turning you into Himself. You become what you eat, and with every Communion, the painting of you becoming more and more like the perfect model child of God comes more and more clearly into view. Our sins and selfish desires ruin the beauty God is trying to restore in us, and so Jesus gives us the sacrament of reconciliation. When we tell Jesus our sins through His priests, we allow Him to go back to work on the perfect picture of Himself He is making in us.

You are all beautiful images of God, and He is grateful you are studying and taking your faith seriously. Your minds are so dear to Him, for this is where you can most brilliantly reflect Him. He will do the work; He holds the two "brushes" that will make you into perfect representations of His Son, the Holy Spirit, and the Blessed Virgin Mary. Remember the Annunciation? At that moment the Holy Spirit came to Mary and in her "yes, the Son of God appeared on earth. This is what can happen to each of us: the Father sends us His Holy Spirit and with Mary we can say "yes" and thus become a son or daughter of God on earth. This is the entire purpose of the Christian faith — to let ourselves to be made into God's children.

— Fr. David Vincent Meconi, S.J.

THEOLOGICAL VIRTUES

SEEING WITH FAITH

GIFT
OF KNOWLEDGE AND UNDERSTANDING

FAITH enables one to know God and all that He has revealed.

Gift of Understanding enables one to see more deeply into the mysteries of the faith and to judge with certainty all created things.

Gift of Knowledge guides one in knowing what to believe and how to share it with others.

ABIDING WITH HOPE

GIFT
OF FEAR OF THE LORD

HOPE enables one to desire God above all things and to trust Him for personal salvation.

Gift of Fear of the Lord enables one to see more deeply into the mysteries of the faith and to judge with certainty all created things.

BURNING WITH CHARITY

GIFT
OF WISDOM

CHARITY enables one to love as God Himself loves, to love God above all things and one's neighbor as oneself.

Gift of Wisdom moves one to order one's life according to God's will.

CARDINAL VIRTUES

ACTING WITH PRUDENCE

PRUDENCE enables one to reason and to act rightly in any given situation — "right reason in action."

Gift of Counsel enables one to respond fully to direction and guidance from the Lord.

— RELATED VIRTUES —

Circumspection: Careful consideration of circumstances and consequences

Foresight: Consideration of the consequences of one's actions; thinking ahead

Docility: Willingness to be taught

LOVING WITH JUSTICE

GIFT OF PIETY

JUSTICE enables one to give to each, beginning with God, what is due him.

Gift of Piety inclines one as a child of God to have devotion and honor to God as Father.

— RELATED VIRTUES —

Affability: Being easy to approach and easy to talk to — friendly

Kindness: Expressing genuine concern about the well-being of others; anticipating their needs

Courtesy: Treating other people with respect, recognizing that all are made in God's image and likeness

Loyalty: Accepting the bonds implicit in relationships and defending the virtues upheld by Church, family, and country

Generosity: Giving of oneself in a willing and cheerful manner for the good of others

Obedience: Assenting to rightful authority without hesitation or resistance

Gratitude: Thankful disposition of mind and heart

Patriotism: Paying due honor and respect to one's country, with a willingness to serve

CARDINAL VIRTUES

Prayerfulness: Being still, listening, and being willing to talk to God as a friend

Respect: Speaking and acting according to one's own and others' rights, status, and circumstances

Responsibility: Fulfilling one's just duties; accepting the consequences of one's words and actions, intentional and unintentional

Sincerity: Trustfulness in words and actions; honesty and enthusiasm toward others

Trustworthiness: Acting in a way that inspires confidence and trust; being reliable

 CONTENDING WITH FORTITUDE

GIFT OF FORTITUDE

FORTITUDE (Courage) enables one to endure difficulties and pain for the sake of what is good.

Gift of Fortitude moves one to endure difficulties for the sake of eternal life with God.

— RELATED VIRTUES —

Industriousness: Diligence, especially in work that leads to natural and supernatural maturity

Magnanimity: Seeking with confidence to do great things in God; literally "having a large soul"

Magnificence: Doing great things for God

Patience: Bearing present difficulties calmly

Perseverance: Taking the steps necessary to carry out objectives in spite of difficulties

MASTERING WITH **TEMPERANCE**

GIFT OF **FEAR OF THE LORD**

TEMPERANCE (Self-Control) enables one to be moderate in the pleasure and use of created goods.

Gift of Fear of the Lord brings forth the fear of offending God by sin.

— RELATED VIRTUES —

Honesty: Sincerity, openness, and truthfulness in one's words and actions

Humility: Awareness that all one's gifts come from God and appreciation for the gifts of others

Meekness: Serenity of spirit while focusing on the needs of others

Moderation: Attention to balance in one's life

Modesty: Purity of heart in action, especially in regards to dress and speech

Orderliness: Keeping oneself physically clean and neat and one's belongings in good order

Self-Control: Joyful mastery over one's passions and desires

Sister Mary Grace Thul, O.P.

My Life in Christ

"Remain in me, as I remain in you. Just as a branch cannot bear fruit on its own unless it remains on the vine, so neither can you unless you remain in me" (John 15:4).

The Dominican saint from the Tuscany region of Italy, Catherine of Siena, gave an analogy that echoes Christ's discourse on the vine and branches. "The soul is in God and God in the soul, just as the fish is in the sea and the sea is in the fish." Just as a fish takes in the sea to survive, so must a disciple remain grafted on the vine to live and bear fruit.

By allowing the Word of God to touch our hearts, we come to know the Person of Christ. Once our minds have grasped the truth of His Words, our hearts follow and we desire only to "remain in His love." The "vineyard" of our heart must be cultivated and tended by the vine grower, who is the Father. The pruning takes place through self-knowledge and identifying the branches deadened by sin and not grafted unto Christ the vine. This requires a personal commitment to free your heart from distractions sin and vice. Sin has deep roots and can strangle the sap of love needed to nourish the branches of virtue.

As you meditate on God's Word, let Him touch your heart and renew your commitment to be His disciple. The path to interior freedom and happiness is found by remaining in Him as a branch grafted on the vine, or in the words of St. Catherine, "The soul is in God and God in the soul, just as the fish is in the sea and the sea is in the fish."

My Life in Christ

Just so, your light must shine before others, that they may see your good deeds and glorify your heavenly Father. Matthew 5:16

DATE _____

_____

_____

_____

_____

DATE _____

_____

_____

_____

_____

DATE _____

_____

_____

_____

_____

DATE _____

_____

_____

_____

_____

My Life in Christ

Just so, your light must shine before others, that they may see your good deeds and glorify your heavenly Father. Matthew 5:16

DATE _____

_____

_____

_____

DATE _____

_____

_____

_____

_____

DATE _____

_____

_____

_____

_____

DATE _____

_____

_____

_____

_____

My Life in Christ

Just so, your light must shine before others, that they may see your good deeds and glorify your heavenly Father. Matthew 5:16

DATE _____

_____

_____

_____

_____

DATE _____

_____

_____

_____

DATE _____

_____

_____

_____

_____

DATE _____

_____

_____

_____

_____

My Life in Christ

Just so, your light must shine before others, that they may see your good deeds and glorify your heavenly Father. Matthew 5:16

DATE _____

_____
_____
_____
_____

DATE _____

_____
_____
_____
_____

DATE _____

_____
_____
_____
_____

DATE _____

_____
_____
_____
_____